By the same author

FICTION

FM247: Radios In Motion

FM247: This Is Radio Binfield!
(co-written with Andrew Worsdale)

RADIO THERAPY

Dear Dave,
Thanks for your ongoing
interest in this world
of music-related
musings — I'll be
looking to get a
Work 'us track in
the next one. :)

All good ones,

Rob

Sept. 2022

Radio Therapy

Published by The Conrad Press Ltd. in the United Kingdom 2022

Tel: +44(0)1227 472 874
www.theconradpress.com
info@theconradpress.com

ISBN 978-1-914913-84-6

Printed and bound in Great Britain by Clays Ltd, Elcograf S.p.A

Typesetting and cover design by The Book Typesetters
www.thebooktypesetters.com

Cover painting 'Moonlight over Porthleven' by Alan Furneaux

The Conrad Press logo was designed by Maria Priestley.

RADIO THERAPY

A musical memoir

Rob Spooner

Dedicated to the memory of
Stephen John Dempsey, 1960–2021

I often think in music. I live my daydreams in music. I see my life in terms of music.

Albert Einstein

PREFACE

This novella has been written as if it were a radio broadcast, with the quotations in italics representing the moments when the primary narrator, Lugwin Loggins, is speaking into a microphone, like a disc jockey. The other unusual use of italics occurs when Lugwin and the secondary narrator, Winston Wyndham, have unspoken thoughts between their spoken words.

The numbering from one hundred to one of the respective chapter titles in descending order symbolises that of a pop music chart. The chapter titles are song titles. The recording artists for these particular tracks are namechecked in the subsequent narrative.

This novella is based on a novel that I co-wrote with Andrew Worsdale, *FM247: This Is Radio Binfield!*, as I wanted to revise aspects of it so that it provided a more coherent prequel to my subsequent novel *FM247: Radios In Motion*. This revision went much further than I had planned and it took on a new direction too. I am very grateful to Andrew who permitted my efforts in revising our original novel in the form of this palimpsest.

Rob Spooner
May, 2022

THE NIGHT SHIFT,
with Lugwin Loggins

'Lugwin – there's enough madness out there without us adding to it.'

They're the words that came back to me on the night that I was admitted to Speedwell hospital, in the countryside several miles west of Binfield-on-Sea, during the summer of 1999. It was Warren, the cheerful staff nurse, who had said them to me many years before, back in 1985. I was twenty-four then. I was a student nurse at Binchley Hatch psychiatric hospital, on the northern outskirts of the city, and it was Warren who was in charge of the night shift.

Warren locked the office door from the inside before he turned off the light. As he did so, he turned back to me and said, 'You see, Lugwin, prevention is so much better than cure.' In the sudden darkness, I could see Warren assembling two chairs to face each other in the form of a makeshift and hard recliner bed. He gestured to the two chairs over my side of the desk and said, 'So, you might as well make yourself comfortable. Otherwise, it's going to be a long night.'

I felt guilty that this was a clear dereliction of our nursing duty but it was so hierarchical in the old psychiatric hospitals back then. If you stepped out of line, the charge nurse would give you a bad report and the staff of the next ward you ended up on would be ready for you. Nico, my best friend from the student nurse group, had suggested the best way to manage this power dynamic: – 'Keep your head down, shut your mouth and box clever. Don't rock the boat 'til you're qualified.' So, I did as I was told but I kept my eyes on the window looking out from the office just in case any patients came out of their rooms and needed a word. Warren was already asleep and snorting out some deep rhythmic snoring couplets.

I stayed awake that night, just like I did on my first night in Speedwell, albeit from the other side of the office window. It wasn't always like that though. Sometimes, the dreamworld would take over and leave me with some bewildering images.

100

Years Ago

When I think of my past, I often associate certain events with the songs that I've loved. This track by Alice Cooper, from his album *Welcome To My Nightmare*, returned to my consciousness a few years ago now – following a dream that I had back in 1994, when I was an in-patient on the St. Piran's Bay acute admissions unit. Or SPiBU, as everyone called it. I suspect this dream was probably fuelled by the various drugs they had me on.

So, there I was in a big concert hall and Alice Cooper is wearing that white suit and top hat that he had for the *Elected* video back in '72. He strides up to the front of the stage and fixes his eyes on me, standing about six rows away. One of the female vocalists calls out my name but she sounds far away. Alice says to me, 'Isn't that our mum calling?' Then the same female vocalist calls out another name, 'Winston'. I haven't heard that name for ages. It was the given name of my best friend Wiz.

Alice looks up towards the back of the hall and says quite sternly, 'Winston – you've got to go home now.'

Some of the light rays from above the stage are turned to

the back of the hall and they seize upon a tall young man with long straggly hair on his way out. I recognise him. It's Wiz. I haven't seen him in years. He still looks as young as he did when I last saw him in 1979. I make my way through the crowd and I try to catch up with him. I get to the foyer just as he's heading down the steps outside. I run through there and shout after him as he hits the street.

'Hey, Wiz – it's not what you think! It's not what you think!'

He keeps walking. He doesn't look back.

I woke up and my pillow was wet from the sweat from the back of my head.

99

Music Man/What's Happening

I told Kenwyn, my 'named nurse', about that dream the next day. He was intrigued and he advised me to note it down and tell Doc Thompson, or 'Tommo' as we called him – but not to his face – in his ward round for the following day. It was really weird. I was getting more and more of these music-related dreams and they all spoke to me about my life, particularly where there were unresolved issues and any uncertainties involved. So, I started this musical memoir which had a connection to the tracks which were influencing my thoughts at various times. This one by The Crazy World of Arthur Brown, released in 1968 as a B-side to *Nightmare*, was a case in point.

I'd been admitted to SPiBU due to a severe depression a couple of months before and I'd found it bewildering to understand what was happening to me. I'd previously been joyful at my move out west to Harbour Head, a fishing village in west Kernow, to be with my girlfriend Donna who'd moved there the previous autumn. After a few weeks of moving in with Donna, I became listless and I felt so negative all the time. I'd had depressive moments before but nothing that stopped me from getting on with life.

So, when Arthur sings of saving 'me' at the end of this track, it reminds me of my decision to put my trust in Kenwyn, Tommo and all the gang on SPiBU to help see me through this difficult time. And luckily, Tommo was right. He told me that 'it may not feel like it just now, but you will feel better eventually.' And after a few more weeks, I went back home to Donna but I had to go to an Out-Patient Clinic in Helstown, a couple of miles inland, to see Tommo. He arranged for me to meet an occupational therapist called Andy who co-opted me into a 'Managing Anxiety and Depression' group on Friday mornings. It was really helpful being amongst other people who'd experienced something similar to me. Andy also encouraged me to write about my musical dream associations and to share some of my musings with the group.

I think that I must have conjoined some of this with a dream that I had about Arthur Brown around this time too. It was another strange one, of course. I dreamt that Arthur was dressed in his trademark stage wear of the late 1960s, with a colander on his head that was ready to sprout flames, just like it did when he performed his legendary Number One hit, *Fire*. The particularly strange thing was that Arthur was at Donna's home, *Homely*, helping me with some decorating whilst she was at work. While we were painting, Arthur asked me questions about the music I liked so I played him some compilation cassettes to give him an idea. This track was on it. Arthur liked that and he said that he hadn't heard it in years. He then gave me a cassette which he'd made and he told me that it reflected my 'musical persona' to him. I don't recall any of that music in the dream but I do remember him saying to me, 'One day, Lugwin, you're going to write a book about your musical memories and you're going to find Wiz again too. It may not feel like it at the moment but you will find him eventually. And he'll have his own music memories too. Of which you will be a big part. And Lugwin, you will be The Emperor. And Wiz will be The Captain. Just like you were in those radio-type cassette broadcasts that you made when you were young boys.'

98

It's Four In The Morning

I continued this musical memoir a few years on in late 1998 following another loss in my life.

I'm aboard *The Southern Star*, a diving vessel moored in the harbour of Harbour Head. It's dark and I can't see a thing. I fumble the light switch and I feel my cat Oscar's fur against my calves. Oscar always wants feeding.

Then I remembered another strange dream from which I've just woken. I'd been holding a tennis racquet. It was one of those old wooden ones from the 1970s. I'd been nervously picking at the catgut strings with the fingers of my left hand. Waiting as my opponent, another boy my own age – about twelve, I think – was about to serve. I was also aware of a woman looking through the nylon fence surrounding the court from just behind me. I wondered why she had stopped to look.

The other boy was familiar but distant. He had an intense demeanour which was slightly shaded by the bright afternoon sun. Behind him, above the grassy bank behind the court, was a silhouetted figure watching from an upstairs window.

My opponent's wide-angled service arrived with swerve and spin but I was just able to deflect the ball back over the net, though only to mid-court. I ran forward in a vain attempt to volley the anticipated return but the other boy lobbed the ball back over my onrushing head and I had to turn quickly to try to retrieve it before its second bounce. I saw the woman looking at my forlorn effort just as I slumped before her. I gasped for breaths that wouldn't come. I could just make out her fingers clutching the mesh on the fence before I glimpsed the starkness of her dejected eyes as she looked away. I think that I fainted in the dream. I'm not quite sure how it ended but I felt anxious and disorientated when I awoke.

I rubbed the moisture from the circular window of the cabin and I saw the bright moon reflecting off the gentle surf in the harbour. Oscar yowled in both a demanding and plaintive tone. I gazed out towards the lights on the far side of the harbour. They continued up the road to where Donna still lives. I checked my alarm and it's just as I thought… four in the morning. That's what I call 'Faron Young time'. And it's still a few hours until the daylight comes.

97

When The Daylight Comes

Good morning. I'm Lugwin. I'm a melancholic and I'm back by myself again. Well, when I say 'by myself', that's not strictly true as my dear cat Oscar is with me aboard *The Southern Star*. He's a lovely cat and he's great company.

The first thing I do when I wake so early, after feeding Oscar, is to put the radio on. There's a show on *Radio Snooze* at that time which really hits the right mood for me. It's relaxed and intimate and it helps me to get into the right groove ahead of doing my own show. I've got it on now. I sometimes joke that I don't listen to my rivals but that's not true.

Bear with me as this might sound strange. I need to explain that I have lived a life inspired by what's coming through those radio airwaves. Take this track now playing by Ian Hunter, from his album *You're Never Alone With A Schizophrenic*, which was released in 1979. It feels like a song of hope and new beginnings. I think that's what I need now. I often retreat back into thinking about what the music provides after I've had an upset. And this time,

21

following my latest loss, it's prompted me to revisit this memoir about where the music takes me. That's since I was shown the door of *Homely* by my ex, Donna. But, right now, Oscar and I need to get on our way below deck where I set up the decks for my stint on a show called *Radio Binfield*.

THE BREAKFAST SHOW,
with Tony Sideburns

My radio hero is the living legend, Tony Sideburns, who launched *Radio Fun* back in 1967. Before I start my shows, I always think of Tony and his sage advice to think that you're talking to just one listener out there. That way, it feels quite intimate. I wrote to Tony once, to tell him that I was an assiduous listener of his *Breakfast Show* before I set off for school back in my hometown, Binfield-on-Sea. That was until it all went horribly wrong on that terrible day when Tony's prized early morning slot on *Radio Fun* was usurped by the hideous interloper, Noel Beardman, in 1973. Tony wrote back to thank me for my letter and he sent me a signed photo of himself from those fab and groovy days. I still have it here in a frame that I place near the mixing desk during my shows. I like to think that he's with me when I speak to that 'one listener' and play some records that he might approve of whilst I attempt to recreate the intimate style of broadcasting that he pioneered all those years ago.

96

Flowers In The Rain

'*Good morning, everyone! Welcome to the exciting new sound of Radio Binfield! A historic day demands historic records, just like this one from The Move which kicked off dear old Radio Fun back in 1967...*'

I am a DJ and there are many records that I play which have a resonance for me. I'd like to tell you about them and their story in my life. Or is it that when I hear them, they evoke those stories? I'm not entirely sure. Take this one, for instance. I woke this morning, half-asleep, with my duvet in a heap as I was sweltering after having that gas heater on all night in the cabin. But I've just gone live on my *Radio Binfield* show and it's here, in a state of almost childish excitement, that you'll find me.

'*... and this is going out to my best friend. We met in the playground that year. I don't know where he is these days but I'll never forget him.*'

95

Spaceball Ricochet

'*From the golden year of 1972, it's from an album called 'The Slider' and it's the solid gold sound of T. Rex!*'

Playing T. Rex records always remind me of The Captain. He was my best friend. And in many ways, he still is, though I haven't seen him for such a long time. Those days when we were in love with T. Rex were our closest times together. Funnily enough, when Marc Bolan and the band went on the wane in '73, that coincided with me and Wiz – that was The Captain's real name, or nickname – drifting apart. The first time.

Well, since I've been back by myself, I've been thinking more about Wiz again and what he might be up to these days. I've also been enjoying this time to myself by making up these compilation cassettes with a bit of talking between tracks just like you'd hear on the radio. Well, me and Wiz, we used to have our own radio station back in those days of 'T. Rex-stacy' and we called it *Radio Binfield*, after our home town of Binfield-on-Sea. We'd make up these cassettes in the style of a radio show together and then make a copy so we'd both have one to listen back to. It was great fun. And I've rediscovered that joy once again since Donna ushered me through the door of her home, *Homely*. Now home is here on *The Southern Star*, courtesy of my pal Ray, who I call The Producer, as he does all the production work on my *Radio Binfield* show.

I'd like to play you this excerpt from one of these new tapes that I've made for The Captain, just in case I ever get to share them with him again. It probably sounds weird, but here goes: –

'Hey, Cap – since I moved out west to Harbour Head, I really discovered how much I love driving. Every day, I'm out and about above the clifftops whizzing around and taking in the fantastic views. And I've always got one of our shows on the cassette player cranking out our favourite songs from the golden years. Take this one, for instance. Marc's wife June said it was about a young boy who was visiting from their neighbour's. June said he had so much energy that he was bouncing off the walls. I guess that was what the 'ricochet' of the title is about, and the chorus too. Oh yeah, the kid was wearing baseball boots so Marc, with his always funky imagination, turned that baseball into 'spaceball'.

But it also reminds me of my brothers, who hated T. Rex. And a day when we're all in my brother Luke's Cortina. I was in the back seat and my brother Jack was in the passenger seat. And it's lucky that Jack was wearing a seat belt. We were out in the Binfield hinterlands, somewhere in the countryside where the roads are fast but also twisty and narrow. On a wider and straighter stretch, we were overtaken by a big car, a bold Jaguar. Luke became annoyed and zoomed up behind the Jag but we needed to slow down as we were fast approaching a roundabout. We didn't slow down enough though and the Cortina nudged the curve of the rounded curb and ploughed onto the roundabout. Time seemed to slow down in that moment and a shimmering haze fell across my eyes as we span over to our left. I saw Jack's still figure suspended in front of me as we careered into the crunching doors. There was shattered glass everywhere. Jack wasn't moving. Luke was shouting. He'd somehow got out and opened the doors over on the driver side.

He seemed far away and the shout of 'Get out! Get out!' sounded like an echo in a valley.

I don't remember how I got out. The next thing I remember was an elderly woman bringing me tea and biscuits whilst I was sitting by the side of a road and wrapped in a blanket. I looked further down the grass verge and I saw an ambulance and two paramedics attending to Jack. Luke was nearby. The Cortina's a crumpled wreck over on the roundabout. The elderly woman saw me looking at it. She said it was lucky that he, referring to Jack, was wearing his seatbelt. I was so relieved when I saw Jack stand up and walk, albeit slowly. Luke patted him on the shoulder and they both headed towards me. We got a cab to a small town nearby – I think it was West Bindown – and then we got the train back to Binfield West. Neither of them said much except when Luke tells me just before we get off the bus for home, 'Not a word to Elsie, Lug. I'll be doing the talking, ok?'

As well as you and my brothers, any T. Rex record always reminds me of my ex, Donna, too. I moved down here to be with her. She loved T. Rex. Well, she loved Marc really. And I think that she did love me too, for a while.

And, Cap, I still feel a great sadness about Marc's untimely

27

death in that car accident back in '77. Do you remember that we became good friends again at that time? Until I lost you for what seems like forever, just a couple of years later. Well, I hope that you'll get to hear this broadcast one day. Hey, I'm doing a real Radio Binfield show now, with thanks to The Producer. I'll tell you about him shortly. But I think that you'd like it.'

94

(Remember The Days Of The) Old Schoolyard

'*I* hope you remember where it all started for us, Cap? In the playground of Binfield Hall, of course. Now this record by Cat Stevens was yet to be released by then but with your love of the kind of record that our hero Tony Sideburns would surely approve of, it's a must for this opening show. I'm going to do a few of them as a kind of homage too to the jocks who I particularly liked on the old Radio Fun of yesteryear.

And talking of yesteryear, let me take you back to that day in '67 when I saw you one morning in the playground, about half an hour before school started. I'd get there early so I could join in the football games with the big boys in order to make up the numbers. You were the first kid there, bouncing a fluffy tennis ball near the goal area that was painted on the wall. You turned to me and said, 'Wanna play six and in?'

So, I said 'Yeah, who's in first?'

You said, 'Me. Take penalties if you want.'

So, you went in goal and I took penalties. I think I'd only taken two or three before some other boys came along and we were able to have a game instead. But we were friends at Binfield Hall from that day onwards.

29

They were great days, Cap. I think about them often. I think a lot about our old friends too and I wonder what happened to them. As well as you, of course. I hope I will be able to see you again one day. I still find it hard to believe that I haven't seen you in so long, but I'm hoping this tape might help to make it happen.'

93

Tiny Children

'This next one, Cap, by Teardrop Explodes, is a little out of keeping with what our breakfast show host Tony Sideburns would have played on Radio Fun back when we were tiny children at Binfield Hall, but I'm playing it for you as it evokes that time and place rather well. You remember our walks to school with our transistor radios pressed to our ears with the loud barks of Tony's dog Arnold, Tony's corny jokes and regular dedications, and his always endearing enthusiasm before he got relegated down the daytime slots all the way to the dreaded graveyard Saturday morning show of Junior Voice? And what about on the way home when the avuncular Fluffy Oldman had to compete with that eerie, off-air transmission jammer of Radio Tirana? How did it go? 'Doo, da-doo, doo, dah do-doo,' I think. It was the sound of far-away Albania calling its expats over on Coney Island, just across the estuary from the western cliffs of Binfield.

I'd call for you down Northbound Grove off the eastern side of Binfield Valley Drive. What a grand road BVD was, as we used to call it. It's lucky we had those lollipop men and women to help us cross it back then, though there was hardly any of the *traffic that you get nowadays. Sometimes after school you'd come over to my place just off the western end of BVD and we'd head down towards the brook, near to where the Thomas twins lived. We loved it down there. Sometimes we'd see Mrs Thomas playing tennis on the grass courts nearby with her constantly changing array of doubles partners. There were plenty of little grubby urchins like us who learned to play on the hard courts instead, next to those grass courts where the club members all played in their spotless whites.*

I loved those summers, Cap. Sometimes, I can still feel the grass around me from when I lay on the bank overlooking the tennis courts. So much of our history is down there and it makes me feel sad wondering now if it's lost forever. And, whilst I sit here now in emotional disarray, thinking of a dream I had when I was playing on one of those hard courts, I think it must have been you who I was playing against in my dream. You were always a better tennis player than me. And how I miss our friendship too.

You know, I also often dream of the brook and its filthy water flowing from the flood defences at its western end near Coney Island all the way eastwards to the glorious waterfront pleasure parks of Binfield-on-Sea, where stands the longest pier in the world. And, even now, I still dream of the magical times that we played down by the brook.

What I also remember clearly is how we lovingly smoked our first cigarettes down by the brook. Just along from the tennis courts to where Southbound Grove meets BVD, under the bridge at the junction. Johnny Regis would get them. Or Johnny Reggae, as we called him, after that novelty record back then. I wonder whatever happened to him? Johnny had such

confidence. I loved the way he'd blag those ciggies from Baines'
newsagents, telling the black-haired, stern-looking woman at
the counter that they were for his mum.

Do you remember that book, 'Coming Up For Air', that our
old English teacher, who we called the Mentor, brought to us,
Cap? It was by George Orwell. I re-read it recently as I've had
a bit more time to myself since I had to leave Donna's place.
It's about a middle-aged man who wonders if that world of his
youth is gone forever. I've been wondering that too lately. But
you know what? I know that I belong there. And, of course, so
do you.'

92

Everyone's Gone To The Moon

'**N**ow I know you're going to love this one. In fact, I remember buying it for you from Guy Norris' Record Store in the Victory Circus shopping precinct at the top of Binfield High Street in the late '70s, back when we were friends again. It was on one of those Old Gold re-issue labels. It originally came out back in 1965 and you told me it was the first record that you could remember being played on the radio. When you spoke about it, circa 1978, you said it was 'doggerel' and also how it spoke to you about your life growing up in Northbound Grove and about being at Binfield Hall too. I didn't know what 'doggerel' meant so I looked it up in the dictionary when I got home.

And, of course, we watched that Apollo moon landing in the big hall at Binfield Hall. And now, every morning when I return to my cabin bed after my early morning constitutional, I'm awake and gazing out of the porthole at the shiny chalk-like coin in the night sky. I always think back to when we watched the space-walks on the black and white telly in the school hall. It was mounted on a tripod for us all to see. But on that historic day back in 1969, the Thomas twins, Pete and

Scott, were nowhere to be seen. That's because they were hiding behind the maroon curtains that adorned the stage in the big hall. And not only that – they were actually embarking on Binfield Hall's crime of the century, whilst we were all transfixed with Neil and Buzz bouncing around on the moon's grey surface. It was quite a juxtaposition of heroism and villainy, Cap. Neil and Buzz embarking on brave new astronomical frontiers and the Thomas twins stealing points sticks from Binfield Hall's meritocracy measurement marker, the Totaliser...'

The Totaliser stood imperiously at the front of the stage on the Friday afternoon assembly before we were allowed home. It was over six feet tall and three feet wide. It was made of oak and it was of totemic significance in Binfield Hall's ethos of fair play and team work. It had four vertical rows where coloured sticks would be placed horizontally and they were arranged in the colours of the school's 'houses' – yellow for Norfolk (Johnny Reggae's house), blue for Oxford (Wiz's house), red for Warwick (my house) and green for Arundel (Pete and Scott Thomas' house).

The Binfield Hall pupils could accrue rewards to be traded in for points on the Totaliser on Friday afternoons. These rewards were bestowed for various orders of merit throughout the week, such as courteous behaviour, walking sensibly down the stairways, kindness towards another pupil or possibly some other random act of good behaviour that was noted by the teachers or prefects. The currency of this recognition was provided in the form of highly-prized merit cards, small cardboard squares that could fit comfortably in your pockets.

On Friday lunch-times, the Headmaster, Mr. Lake,

would work out the ratio of merit cards to the particular houses that the card-carrying pupils represented. In that afternoon's assembly, the great unveiling of the point sticks totals would take place. Seven coloured sticks were awarded to the victorious house for that week, five sticks to the runner-up house, three sticks to the house that came third and a single stick to the house that had accrued the least merit cards.

It was coming up to the last Friday before the end of term and the Thomas twins' house, Arundel, was just nudging behind Oxford towards the finish line. The Totaliser was always placed behind the maroon velvet curtains up on the stage in the assembly hall during the week until its great unveiling on Friday afternoons. The Thomas twins had been spotted going towards the back stage door whilst we were watching the moon landings in the hall. Mr Lake ascended the stage quickly and slipped behind the maroon curtain where he caught Pete Thomas blue-handed whilst he was taking point sticks from the Oxford column. It was an audacious effort to subvert the school's credo and it certainly cast Pete Thomas and Scott, to a lesser degree, in the Binfield Hall 'hall of shame' on the final Friday of term when the last points sticks were slotted into place.

That was an impressive gesture of public shaming by Mr. Lake on that decisive Friday in the Totaliser's totting-up of the final point stick tally – making the Thomas twins place the sticks into the columns at his behest! They were quite a pair those two, eh Cap? Dear old Scott with his customary nonchalance and funny old Pete with his quirky ways. Pete had a terrible temper at times and you had to watch out for its potential

36

eruption. *I always got on better with Scott and I used to meet him down in the Old Town years later. But that's another story. And, oh yes, talking of other stories, this record was of course a debut hit for the infamous Jonathan King. Before our time, I know, but I looked it up in my book of British Hit Singles and I see that it got to number four in the charts.'*

91

Back Home

'*T*his *one by the England World Cup Squad of 1970 is another of those records that transports me back to what I now think of as the happiest days of my life. Released on the lovely light blue Pye label of the time, it's a rousing call to arms. Or more accurately, feet. I hope that you'll like hearing it again...*'

I used to love those play-times at Binfield Hall. As we got nearer to Fridays, the football games that we played would take on an ever greater, manic urgency. Especially when Mr. Newsome, who picked the school's teams, was on playground duty. He used to sit on one of those green benches that separated the playground from our field of dreams, the school's well-tended football pitches.

Mr. Newsome didn't say much but I saw that he observed everything from his roaming, hawkish eyes that sat astride his ant-eater's nose. He cut an imposing figure. He was tall and slim and still had youthful freckles which somehow compensated for his thinning auburn hair.

We were all in awe of Mr. Newsome. He had the power to make or break our week-ends. We strove to impress him in our lunch-time games when he was on playground duty, especially when Friday approached. Friday was the day of decision – it was the day when the school's football team-sheets went up on the noticeboard by the toilets opposite the cloak-rooms at Binfield Hall. I remember gripping the wooden hand-rail that bordered the stairway down to the noticeboards in sweaty anticipation on those Friday lunch-times and when I saw my name on the team-sheet, scribed in Mr. Newsome's ornate calligraphy, it made my heart beat faster and gave me a wondrous warm surge inside. I'd almost skip in glee to the school canteen after I saw my name there. But you couldn't overdo it if one of your friends hadn't been picked. Like when Wiz had been left out the week that 'Ginger' Moore had been put in at right back instead. And Ginge couldn't even trap the ball! I tried to console Wiz by suggesting that Ginge was Newsome's nephew as they had similarly coloured hair. But Wiz couldn't be consoled. He was really hurt by his omission. He said he was 'gonna show Newsome, no matter what it takes.'

After Wiz sloped off morosely down Northbound Grove that Friday after school, I adorned the team shirt, with its glorious maroon and white hoops, over my shoulders and walked faster in my efforts to catch up with Lorraine Robinson and her friends. With that shirt's hooped arms festooned around my neck and its black number eight draped across my back, I felt like a mini-caped superhero. I so hoped that Lorraine would turn around and see me before we went our separate ways at the top of Binfield Valley Gardens, or BVG, the road where she lived. And I just about got near enough when she waved and smiled as she and her sister Louise headed off down BVG.

The next morning, we had a game over in east Binfield at a school called Binchurch. Wiz came along with his grandad to watch. Wiz didn't have a dad but we never spoke about that. Or his absent mum either. We didn't know what the story was there.

We were a player short as Scott Thomas hadn't turned up. We found out on Monday back at school that Mrs. Thomas had kept him home as he'd been tormenting his twin, Pete. Johnny Reggae was our captain and he asked Mr. Newsome if Wiz could play as Wiz had come along in his kit, just in case. I saw Mr. Newsome shrug his shoulders and give an insouciant kind of look before he said 'Okay – but out on the right wing.' Wiz was delighted though. He said he'd never played up front before and now he was 'gonna show Newsome' what he could do. Wiz didn't have a school shirt as he wasn't due to play but Mr. Newsome had a spare one without a number and he threw it to him.

It was one of the best games we played. Johnny Reggae was brilliant that day and he scored a hat-trick. I didn't congratulate him on any of his goals though as I'd heard that he'd been seeing Lorraine alone down by the brook. Also, Wiz nicked one at the far post from a cross of mine. He ran half the length of the pitch after scoring and stuck two fingers up at Mr. Newsome as he'd seen George Best do it to a referee on *The Big Match*. Sadly, that was the last time that Wiz played for the first team.

'Possibly a bittersweet one for you, Cap... but even so, I loved playing football with you and it needs to be said that you

were a far better player than Ginger Moore. You know that Mr. Newsome was his uncle, don't you?'

90

The Saturday Boy

'I'll never forget the first and only time that I took her out, Cap. Her sister Louise came along too. There were only three tickets and my Mum told me that I was to give you one of them but when Louise heard about it, I gave in to her pleading and I gave your ticket to her. This track by Billy Bragg was released many years after the summer of '71 when this momentous event in my life happened but it evokes the time and sentiments perfectly. We were nearing the end of the school holidays. It was Carnival Week in Binfield and the circus was back in town. This tale of unrequited love that Billy sings of stirs both happy and sad feelings in me and always reminds me of Lorraine, the girl who nearly every boy in our year had a crush on. She was the first girl I knew who wore hot pants. And they certainly had that effect, even on a pre-pubescent, not quite eleven-year-old.

The sisters wore shiny red plastic macs that night as there was a forecast of rain. Mrs. Robinson drove us to the carnival over at Binfield Common. I sat between them in the Big Top and I felt like a member of an infant aristocracy whilst surveying this grand spectacle of slapstick clowns, dancing horses and a ringmaster with a booming voice, amidst those red-mac clad Robinson girls. The rain did fall but we were spared the worst of it inside the huge canvas amphitheatre.

Mrs. Robinson was there waiting outside with her umbrella as it finished and she took us home in her car. My mum must have been working at the pub that night as it was dark when Mrs. Robinson dropped me off and I had to let myself in with the spare key which was tucked away in the cat food box in the porch. And then, lo and behold the wonderful memory, Lorraine had followed me in there and gave me a lovely kiss to thank me for taking her to the circus. Ah, Cap... though I felt bad about your ticket, that moment is still one of my childhood treasures. But there was only one Johnny Reggae, of course, and there were no more moments alone with Lorraine. Besides, when we got back to school that September, she'd cut her hair. And that was that. I stopped loving her.

89

Have You Seen Her?

'*I* recall you always liked records with talky-bits in them, Cap, and I remember that you included this one by The Chi-Lites in one of our home broadcasts back in early '72. Well, it came back into view for me earlier this week when I was sitting on a bench at the top of the hill above Harbour Head. It may not have looked that good to any other adult nearby as it wasn't far from a children's play area just down below. I like it up there though. You get great views looking out over the mighty Atlantic Ocean, or at least the Mount's Bay part of it. But it's her face I see everywhere I look. That's Donna who I came out here to be with. Donna Raven. You'd like her, Cap. She's so full of vitality, but sadly, one month before that day I was sitting on that bench earlier this week, I was a vital part of her life no longer.

But it's you who I wish was here with me now. And this broadcast is part of trying to compensate for that loss. Those children down in the play area remind me of us and our gang back at Binfield Hall. You know, some of those kids even know my name. They call up 'Hi Lugwin' and they try to impress me with their gymnastics on the climbing frame overhanging the

44

sand-pit. Their parents know me so it's all ok. In fact, I seem to be getting well known here in Harbour Head. It's ever since I started my Radio Binfield slot on the local radio. I've even had people come up asking if it's me who does all the records with the memory stories. And I signed my autograph for a fan of the show last week too! I'm feeling more of a sense of belonging here now, Cap. But it's not always been easy and like with any loss, you just have to get used to it.'

88

I'm Stone In Love With You

'I guess it's confession time here, Cap. And this is the joy of these personal radio broadcasts because what I say into this mic' feels a whole lot easier than saying it face to face. Though I really do hope that I get to do so before we get much older. Now, this one by The Stylistics might seem an unexpected choice as neither of us were fans of theirs back in '72. However, I've re-appraised them following my picking up of their 'Best Of' compilation in one of the charity shops in Harbour Head the week after Donna bade me farewell from her bungalow. And I think this is a wonderful track. I hope that you do too.

That line about being a movie star cracks me up. I know that it's somewhat 'mock-heroic', as the Mentor used to say, about seeing ourselves in such a deluded fashion but with this almost local hero fame that I've somehow had placed on me lately, I'm feeling a slight buzz from this minor celebrity status that I've recently acquired.

It reminds me of when we were the big kids at Binfield Hall, in that final year before we had to go off to the awful grammar school, Pouk Hill, and start at the lowest rung all over again. That place seemed to drive a wedge between us *somehow. We were in different classes for a start and somehow or other, I don't really know the reason why, you turned against me and my whole world was turned into a darker place. And now we've been apart for so long, I miss you even more. In all the years in between, I've been able to learn how to express myself more honestly without too much embarrassment. So, my dear Cap, I can assure you that this much is true... I love you and miss you more than I think you could ever know.'*

87

Kung Fu Fighting

'They were tough times during my social isolation in the early days of Pouk Hill, Cap. The nadir was when I came up against Dave Paynter, the brother of Graham. You'll recall that Dave was a year older than us and also Graham, who was in our year. Dave joined my class-mates in a game of football down on the bottom field one lunch-time. Despite not being in our class, he felt entitled to do so as Graham was playing. He was always a bit lairy was Dave. And he liked to push it. Anyway, I chested the ball down and then he suddenly barged into me and appealed for handball before punching me on the arm and telling me, 'It hit you there.'

I then made a big mistake. I punched him in the chest and said, 'No – it hit me there.'

It all went a bit hazy after that. He smacked me a cracker in my left eye. I couldn't see properly but I know that I tried to hit him with a flailing right hook to his head. I don't think that I connected as I'd have liked. Either way, he then caught me with three further head shots before he stopped as I couldn't defend myself. I was relieved that he did. I was pretty dazed and sloped off to the bogs to clean myself up. My top lip was *already ballooning and when I got back into class for the after-noon lessons, the kids in front of me all turned around to gawp at my battered face. I felt like an exhibit at a freak show.*

So, Cap, I don't know if you ever got beaten up there, but when I hear this one by Carl Douglas, it always takes me back to Pouk Hill in 1974 and the day that Dave Paynter gave me a pasting.'

86

The Boys Are Back In Town

'Things took a turn for the better, Cap. Especially by the early summer of '76 when I discovered discos. There was a particularly good one that took place aboard a large boat called the Bembridge, a cruising pilot vessel moored on the eastern side of the Old Town. Ah, it was a whole new world stepping up onto that gangplank to the big boat and being assailed by the various scents of cheap perfume and that dear old male equivalent, Brut 33 'splash-on lotion'. It was the era when boys wore high-waisted baggies and florid, big-collared shirts. Some of the girls wore denim skirts and stack shoes and their make-up made them look a lot older than they were. I know that because I saw Louise Robinson there and she was a year younger than us. She would have been fourteen then, but she looked at least seventeen.

I'd been lured onto the Bembridge by a fellow Pouk Hill pupil by the name of Ben Trippier. You'll remember Ben, I'm sure. Possibly the tallest lad in our year at six-foot-four. I got to know him when we moved to Beastwood the year before. We braved the Beastwood lads on the way home together but it was okay as he'd been to the primary school there and he knew *most of their 'tough nuts', so we generally got home without too much difficulty…'*

Beastwood was out on the north-west fringes of Binfield-on-Sea and still part of Binfield, which was a big borough comprising various districts. I think of it topographically as the northern tip of a triangle with Binfield town centre to the south-east and the Old Town, with its cobbled street on its south-western tip, circa three miles from both the town centre and Beastwood. Beastwood was a relatively modern part of town at that time and most of the housing there was built in the 1920s, though there were quite a few new houses built in the 70s in streets named Buzz Aldrin Way and Neil Armstrong Close. We moved there when my brothers Luke and Jack had left the family home and Mum had decided that she was going to make a go of it with this guy Ted who lived over the road from us in Binfield Valley Drive. The only snag about staying there was that Ted was still married, so that was another reason for moving out to 'the sticks' in Beastwood.

'It was a great feeling of freedom and anticipation heading towards those discos on a Friday night, Cap. Pouk Hill, as you well know, felt so oppressive, what with its archaic self-importance and pompous airs. The only redeeming features of the place were the younger teachers who weren't imbued with that condescending demeanour that characterised the old guard. Though even amongst that old guard, 'Tosser', the History teacher, had a colonial charm and his drawling voice was quite comforting. When he droned on in his seemingly endless monologues, I could feel my eyes closing and I'd drift off into a harmonious reverie until he suddenly wished to elicit a

response to whatever it was that he'd been talking about. Then, if he caught one of us snoozing, he'd chuck his chalkboard rubber at the dozing miscreant. I like to think that's how dear old Tosser got his nick-name.

So, it was a blessed relief to be heading out on a Friday night and leaving all that Pouk Hill dragging me down misery or sending me off to sleep boredom behind for the week-end. I'd meet Ben down by the alleyway leading into Beastwood Park before we headed off to the Old Town. There were hints of what a great summer it was going to be as the air felt very warm, even at seven o'clock in those spring evenings.

This record by Thin Lizzy had been out for a little while and it was being played all the time on Radio Fun. I loved it. And I still do. I remember my own disco uniform at the time. Black baggy trousers with three grey pinstripes, cherry red Doc Martens polished up with a black tinge and usually a garish shirt, but without a big collar. Ben used to love wearing a blue velvet jacket. It wasn't exactly orthodox clobber for what the kids wore around our way but it did suit him. He used to wear a more upmarket aftershave than most, a pleasing aromatic little number called Aramis. He too looked much older than his age, not least because of his height, but because his facial hair was quite advanced too. And he was confident with the girls, a trait that has clearly stayed with him, as I'll tell you more of a bit later. In the meantime, let's crank this one up nice and loud!'

85

Saturday Night Beneath The Plastic Palm Trees

'**I** don't know about you, Cap, but all that time at a boys-only grammar school had seriously undermined any 'at ease-ness' that I felt amongst girls in those mid-teenage years. It took what felt like an anxious age before I acquired any semblance of confidence in that domain. I think that's when I developed my alcohol dependency in trying to cope with the social anxiety of those disco nights on the Bembridge. The first stop there was at the bar, though Ben and I had already downed a bottle of cider between us on the walk through the woods towards the Old Town. Ben seemed to get drunk even quicker than me despite his much bigger physique. Although maybe my 'squat' build, as he called it, may have had hidden advantages in my greater ability to metabolise the effects of the alcoholic apple juice. Who knows? He was funny when he was drunk though. Ben never turned nasty like some drunk people and he really was a very happy drunk. He'd always have some acerbic per-spective that would emerge freely once he'd been on the cider and that if he'd been sober, he'd probably have kept to himself. He also didn't seem to mind rejection by the girls for any dances. It was all part of the fun of those nights on the Bem-

bridge. And it was Ben who told me that Louise had been eyeing me up during that first night on the old pilot vessel. It was great to see her again after all these years. I looked towards her and gave her a little smile. She nodded, took a sip from her drink and then carried on talking to her friends.'

I thought that I'd best stop there in relaying any more details back to Wiz on this broadcast. You see, it's been a major sore point for us owing to what happened a few years later. Wiz was with Louise for a couple of years before he went missing. And I think that he blamed me for a mis-understanding that occurred back then. That also happened in the Old Town, in an alleyway just off its main cobbled street near Ye Olde Smack Inn, known locally as 'the Smack.' Louise had got drunk and she'd fallen over. I'd gone to help her up and I managed to get her arm over my shoulder whilst I held onto her waist. She was laughing and trying to kiss me as I held her closer, just to straighten her up and to try to get her walking, at least into the main street from where I could call a cab.

I didn't know that Wiz had been watching. It was Scott Thomas who told me just after I'd managed to guide Louise onto one of the chairs under the railway bridge. Scott had been drinking outside the Smack and said that Wiz had stormed off 'looking in a ghastly mood with whatever was going on with you two'. I rang for a cab from the call-box just outside the pub whilst Scott kept an eye on Louise. And then I never saw Wiz again.

'Well, it was on Friday nights that I used to go those Bem-bridge discos and it was in the Old Town rather than Totten-ham Hale, but this record by the Leyton Buzzards and its story

about being drunk on cider whilst at a disco always transports me back to those heady times. It was a record that you brought to my attention too. I still love it. And I wonder if you do too?'

84

Avenues and Alleyways

'Just mentioning Louise there, Cap, brought it all back for me and the night in '79 that you disappeared from my life. Scott Thomas told me that you'd been there in the Old Town when she was drunk in that alleyway near the Smack, and that you'd stormed off after what you'd seen. Well, I know that it's very late for you to be hearing this, but nothing happened between us. I was just trying to help her up as she was in a bad way. She'd joined me and Scott for a drink out the side of the pub and she was already tipsy. She told me that she'd split up with you and I know that she felt bad about that. She said that there was another guy involved, someone who'd had an interest in her for a while and what with you heading off to university at the end of the school holidays, she thought that she'd take a chance. She was drinking that horrific Pernod stuff and it reacted badly with whatever she'd had before. I didn't see it happen myself as I was in the gents at thew time but Scott said that she got up to go to the loo and she staggered out the wrong way, tottering over towards the alleyway. And that's where I found her. And well, you know what you saw, I guess. Maybe I should have let her sleep it off there like a baby, Cap, *but it didn't seem right. I managed to get her in a cab and then to her door. Mrs. Robinson wasn't too impressed. As I gather you weren't either. And sadly, I've never seen you since.*

I'm so truly sorry about what happened. You may recall that this one was the theme to The Protectors. Well, I was just trying to protect Louise from any further loss to her compromised dignity that night. I won't mention this incident again and, as I often say when I'm doing my Radio Binfield show, it's time for less talk and more music... so, get yourself ready for the mighty Tony Christie!"

83

Misunderstood

'**N**ow I always associate this one with Scott Thomas, or 'Scotch' Thomas as he became once I discovered his predilection for the ginger demon. I used to see him down the Old Town and hang out with him in that summer before I went off to college up in the city. That's also where he'd started work after we all left Pouk Hill. So, we'd occasionally meet up there too. He really didn't want to have too much to do with his twin Pete and he was very much his own man. Scotch had become a rough mix of abrasive and gregarious and he was decidedly self-directed, rarely committing to anything that required bending to anyone else's rules or an expectation of his conformity.

Scotch loved this track by Pete Townshend which was on an album that Pete recorded with his friend Ronnie Lane, 'Rough Mix', and which was released in '77. Scotch was great company back then, Cap. He eschewed any dalliances with people who he couldn't abide and his put-downs were the most withering that I've ever heard. I was just relieved that I was one of the people who he didn't cut down with that sharp tongue of his. Even when he did start pointing it towards me,

I'd hear the humour first, so it never felt truly personal or hurtful. But not everyone got it and that's why he was often misunderstood. But he liked it like that. I think that it helped him to build quite a protective veneer for himself and also keep that little bit of personal distance and autonomy which was important to him. He was a generous and loyal friend though and I've missed him since coming out here to Harbour Head a few years ago.

What with Scotch staying in Binfield and commuting up to the city in those early days of your missing years, he'd keep me posted on any developments, such as whether you'd been seen and so on. There were various reports that you'd been sighted under one of the bridges down at the brook or living rough in a wooded area below the Wrestling Fields, near Binfleet Castle. It was all rumour, of course, and no-one had actually seen you up close to speak to.

I did try to keep in touch with your grand-parents during the year after but they were devastated by your disappearance and I gradually lost touch with them after I opted to stay up in town in a poky little flat in Rectory Grove that shuddered every time a train rushed through the station nearby. I often wondered about you though and I tried to fathom what it was that could make you wish to go off like you did. It felt that it must be about more than the incident of which I will no longer speak. I've never understood how it could come to that. But I hope to find out one day.'

82

The Poacher

'*I don't know about you, Cap, but I love the music of Ronnie Lane. This one's from the days when Ronnie was out on the road with his band Slim Chance and when they played gigs in circus tents as part of their 'Passing Show'. Some of Ronnie's music from his albums of the seventies has a kind of fairground feel to it, and I love this one with its haunting horns and silky strings. It's the title though that makes me think of Ben Trippier, who Scotchy re-named 'Bonk Tripego' after Ben's assorted dalliances and consequent bragging about them...*'

I thought that there was something suspect about Ben when I discovered him down by the entrance to Beastwood Park ahead of one of our rendezvous' looking over towards a small block of flats nearby. He was so rapt in checking out whatever was there that he didn't hear me approach him. I startled him as I reached up to his shoulder to give him a playful cuff.

'Hey Ben, what's up? What you looking at?'

'Oh, Luggy – just look over there, first floor, second right window.'

I scanned across and saw an open window without any

blinds or curtains up. A young woman was undressing.

'Ben – you're a bad lad. C'mon, let's away.'

He wanted to stay though. I had to walk towards the main road before he'd leave the scene. I wouldn't say that I was particularly moralistic or anything like that, but that kind of prurient voyeurism has never really been my thing. Maybe it's part of a hankering for the 'decency' that Orwell wrote of in *Coming Up For Air*. Maybe it was something to do with greater respect for women generally as my mum was the key adult influence in my early life, having been my single parent for several years before Ted came along. Even though I wasn't sure of how that feeling of respect for women arrived, I was always wary of the objectification issues that several of my male friends seemed to have back then. I think now that Ben was probably a sex addict but we hadn't really come across labels like that back in the mid-seventies.

'Well, this probably isn't any news to you now, Cap, but that mystery man who Louise had been pestered by back before your split was none other than Ben Trippier. I think that he made it his business to be a bit of a poacher in territory where he really shouldn't have strayed. I'll tell you a bit more about that kind of activity in a little while. In the meantime, prepare to be transported back to Ronnie's wonderful lyricism, including that joyous imagery of fishing by the river with its echoes of Orwell's Lower Binfield revisited via his protagonist George Bowling's hankering for those lost, carefree days of his youth and the decency that I still try to aspire to.'

81

Solitaire

'**W**ell, Cap, we're going to finish our homage to Tony Side-burns and his legendary breakfast show with a sad song. It was released in the year that Tony was replaced on the prime slot by that interloper Noel Beardman. As you remember, Tony took over from Jimmy Recipe on the housewives' show, as it was called somewhat archaically back then. It all went downhill somewhat quickly for Tony as his marriage floundered and he was then consigned to less popular slots in the schedules over the next ten years before leaving Radio Fun in 1984. I always think of Tony as one of the greatest living DJs of our times and I continue to heed his advice 'to think of that one listener' out there when broadcasting. It really helps to give the shows the intimacy that's required to ensure that this medium remains so valuable to the great listening public.

This is the only Andy Williams record that I have in my col-lection. It's on the gorgeous red CBS label and it's a bit crackly now. Do you remember Andy with his avuncular sweaters and calm delivery? He had his own TV show too, which also fea-tured a regular character called 'Cookie Bear'.

So, here's wishing you a farewell from Radio Binfield tem-

porarily with this first cassette broadcast and I will be starting on a new show for the next time slot soon. I'm hoping to get Oscar to purr into the mic' as we say goodbye for now. Ah, fantastic! He's as natural a performer as Andy's Cookie Bear! And though it's just me as the lone jock in the studio currently, Cap, please remember our saying: you're never alone with Radio Binfield. Stay tuned and don't touch that dial!'

OUR TUNES,
with Simon Mates

Simon Mates used to present the mid-morning show on *Radio Fun* in the late 1970s right through to the early '90s. I was mainly able to listen to it in the early '80s due to the occasional later starts when I was at college and then subsequently when I took up some shift-work, which led to me working some afternoons and nights. 'Simes', as he was known, always had such a kindly delivery and the highlight of his charming show was the sometimes mawkish *Our Tune* slot where he invited the listeners to share a story which they had related to a particular record. I think that the *Our Tune* slot most inspired the latter-day incarnation of *Radio Binfield*, the radio show that I'm presenting in honour of Simes and my other favourite jocks. I'd like to thank Simes for his great inspiration and I'm so glad to hear that he's still delivering great shows over on the regional radio frequencies.

80

Gonna Make You A Star

'**H** ey, Cap – I'm going to try to spare the blushes of a special guy who's here in the studio with me and Oscar. I've only mentioned him briefly to you but he's the man who brought me to *The Southern Star* and he is also the producer of my Radio Binfield show on this soon-to-be community radio station that we've got happening here in Harbour Head. He knows so much about all these tech things that I duff constantly and without him I'd be all at sea – rather than just floating around here in the harbour.

So, let's cue the fantastic music – it was from the film 'Romeo and Juliet', wasn't it? – that Simes used to start his 'Our Tune' slot with. 'Der-der-der-der'… and away we go.

Picture the scene if you will. A portly middle-aged man is sitting on a bench and looking out over the harbour. He appears to be very sad, judging by his saturnine expression. Just a half hour or so ago, his true love had told him that he needed to find somewhere else to live. He didn't know what he would do. He was at a loss, and not for the first time in his thirty-eight years too. She'd been kind about it. He didn't need to leave immediately but he had to go. He wanted to stay in

65

Harbour Head. Despite his early difficulties with his acclimat-
isation to a different way of life out here, he knew that it was
where he wished to be, at least for now. Whilst he was lost in
maudlin contemplation, he heard a car pulling up nearby and
then a door shutting…'

'Hey, Lugwin. What's up, mate?'

I looked up and saw my friend Ray. He was wearing his fab black leather jacket and he looked kindly and concerned.

'It's Donna, Ray. She's chucked me out.'

'Ah, mate. Sorry to hear that.' He patted me on the shoulder and sat alongside me. 'You see that big boat in the outer harbour?'

'Wow, it's hard to miss that beauty. What about it?'

'I've taken it on. There's a cabin there that's yours if you want it. It'll be a bit cold at the moment but I can get a gas heater in and it should make it nice and warm.'

I was really taken aback. I'd only known Ray a short while through a pub quiz up we participated in at The Atlantic pub over on the eastern side of the harbour and overlooking Mount's Bay. He was really impressed by my music knowledge, though it was only really good for a particular era, from the late-sixties to the early-eighties.

'Ray, that's incredibly kind of you. I'd love being aboard that wonderful ship. You called it a big boat but it's like the 'Mon Amigo' to me – you know, the ship that Radio Mariline used to broadcast from?'

'Ah – well, it's funny that you should say that, Lug, my amigo. Because I've got plans to do a few radio shows from there. And I think that you, with your music knowledge and enthusiasm, could be just the person I'm looking for to launch the station.'

'Wow. I can't believe that I'm hearing this. I've had an unfulfilled ambition to be a DJ for much of my life. I used to pretend to be one with my best mate when we were kids. And this sounds like a dream come true. You've made my day, Ray. And you can most definitely count me in!'

'Brilliant, Lugwin! Come with me and I'll show you around.'

Well, you've probably guessed, Cap, that I was, and still am, that portly middle-aged man and after The Producer came over to check how I was, we got in his car and this record by David Essex came on the radio. As I'm musing on David's cheeky grin, his knowing wink and his boyish charms, as was the case back in 1974, The Producer turns to me and said, 'You know what, Lugwin? I think that you're a star and I just know that you are going to love it on The Southern Star. And I do love it here, Cap. I'm immensely grateful to Ray, The Producer, for providing me with a berth here and for the birth of my fledgling DJ career. Now here's David...'

79

I'm Not Down

'**I**'d like to tell you about Donna, Cap, and how this schism
arose. I didn't see it coming but she explained that she
found it hard to adapt to the uncertainty of whether my
mental health problems might resurface after I had a spell in
the acute unit a few miles up the road from here. She said that
she wouldn't be able to manage any difficulties that I had as
well as trying to hold down her stressful work with children
with special needs. I felt that I'd been doing ok as I certainly
wasn't down but I was still only back to working part-time for
a voluntary organisation in what I now jokingly refer to as
'charity' work, because we DJs like to be seen to do our bit for
charity. However, the organisation that I work for is a real
charity set up to help older people and it is concerned with
their welfare. Thus, its name of Age Concern. I've still
managed to keep the job on with my DJ commitments here
and I enjoy visiting socially isolated elders before trying to
arrange for volunteer befrienders to provide social support to
them on a regular basis.

I met Donna when I was working in a 'Mental Health Project' back when I was in the city. It involved a bit of sitting

around chatting with the folks who popped in from the locality around there. There were three estates all close by and the 'drop-in centre' of the 'Project' opened every week-day morning through to the lunch-time period and also on Wednesday evenings. All sorts of people came through those doors for a cuppa and a chat and some even joined therapy groups at the Project or attended sessions of individual counselling. Donna was a social work student back then and she'd come to the Project for her 'placement' in a mental health 'setting'. Ah, all those strange words and peculiar phrases from the world of 'social care', Cap...'

It was a sunny October morning when I opened the drop-in and the sunlight shone brightly through the big window at the front of the building. I was catching up with some of the gang following the week-end and hearing what they'd been up to. Sometimes not very much, due to aspects of their particular situation. It was a relaxed atmosphere in there that morning. Then the door opened from the main part of the building and my supervisor Larry introduced me to a long, dark-haired young woman who was dressed mainly in black, with a particularly alluring lacy top. She appeared confident with a smiling demeanour and she had quite iridescent eyes that seemed to change from green to hazel depending on whether the sunlight was on them.

I learned later that she used to be the lead singer in a band, Mad Donna and The Sliders, and that she had a background in drama with a young people's theatre group. She would have been in her mid-twenties by the time she arrived in my life via that side door and now she'd decided to commit herself to the brave new world of 'community care' that was developing in the late eighties.

'It was a few years before we got together, Cap. I was with someone at that time – in fact, I got married to her shortly after. That didn't work out too well and we split up within a year of tying that rickety knot. But Donna and I kept in touch during those years and I eventually moved out west to Harbour Head to be with her. I felt so at ease down here. It was a joy to be out of the hubbub of the city and we got along really well back then. We did have plans to have a child together but that never happened. I doubt that I'd have been suited to being a father anyway.

This one by The Clash, from their album 'London Calling', was actually recorded near to where the Project was situated. The Clash and their roadies used to play football in the playground of the school which bordered the nearest estate to the Project. That was in the summer of '79 though, way before I used to sit around in the drop-in nearly ten years later.

But despite me not being down at that time, I couldn't convince Donna that she had nothing to worry about with my depression anymore. What had brought up her fears for the future, I think, was that I was briefly dependent on her again when I was laid up after a cartilage operation and that brought back reminders of her needing to be strong enough to look out for me rather than the other way 'round. And also, when she came back from a late shift to find out that I was in a sleepy drunk state after going out on my crutches with some of the guys I knew from playing five-a-side football. She was really annoyed about that as she had been working on maintaining her sobriety at that time.

So, I'm trying really hard not to be on a downer about the split with Donna. On the plus side, I can play my old Clash records as loud as I like now.'

78

Far Far Away

'**C**ap – I don't hold any bad feelings towards Donna for how things turned out. I'm actually really grateful to her. She made it happen for me to be here. And my feeling is that Harbour Head is where I want to be. However, the onset of that depression just after moving here a few years ago certainly sent me reeling.

So, here's how it developed. I'd been here for a few months. Donna found me a job with the Child Protection Team where I'd have to work on investigations into reported child abuse and go 'doorstepping' the parent or parents concerned. I really wasn't equipped to deal with some of the fall-out of those situations though, especially when it involved the upset of some children being taken into foster care. Also, not being a parent myself, I felt totally unqualified to be having any kind of judgement call in relation to the parenting skills of the parents who I met in the course of the work. It had a swift and adverse effect on my self-esteem.

Although I really wanted to be with Donna out here, the work precipitated a lot of the anxiety that triggered my spiral into the depression. It got so bad that I couldn't make any *decision. I'd be staring into the wardrobe trying to work out what clothes to wear. I'd lay in the bath and found that I had no energy to get out. When it reached its worst stage, I'd try to speak but no words would come. People would be talking to me and I couldn't actually work out what they were trying to tell me. I was far, far away and my thoughts were so clouded. I stopped going to work after I felt that I couldn't manage it any longer. I'd lost all sense of who I was but I knew also that I didn't like who I was. I had such a downer on myself and I gave myself a really hard time. It was a bad place to be. It was so bad that even Slade couldn't lift me out of it...'*

77

Dear Elaine

'*What I discovered in the course of my treatment on the acute unit, SPiBU, was that the depression was probably precipitated by ongoing uncertainty and cumulative loss. Despite my initial joy at being with Donna in Harbour Head, the situation was always a bit uncertain because of her volatility of mood and also because my job was only a temporary contracted one. Doc Thomson, or 'Tommo', had noted that I'd had much loss in my life, and he was keen to explore some situations with me. He asked me about my failed marriage to Elaine. That's Elaine Knowles, Cap. You'd have liked her...*'

It's still strange to think of how quickly Elaine and I drifted apart after getting married. It was almost as if the marriage led to our split but, on reflection, I think that we'd started drifting before then. We'd moved into a flat in an area called Booting. It was one of those city districts that hadn't yet been gentrified during the late-1980s and from what I've heard from my old friends still living there, it hasn't done so even now. I quite like that. And I liked living there too. Until the cold shoulder nights and the disdain that I felt from Elaine.

Elaine was much more ambitious than me. We'd met when she was working at Binfield General Hospital. She was a staff nurse and she'd been looking after my mum before Mum died. I recall seeing her for the first time in January '85. I saw her as I approached Mum's side room. There she was, with the striking and contrasting colours of her curly ginger hair nestling above the regulation turquoise tunic of her uniform, and sitting at the end of Mum's bed. Elaine was talking to Mum at the start of the visiting period when I arrived. They were laughing together. It was nice to see as Mum had been very poorly and, at one stage, we didn't think that she was going to pull through. She had angina and it was very difficult for her to breathe when those episodes were acute. But whatever Elaine had said to her that afternoon certainly had a positive effect.

Elaine told me she loved me shortly after Mum's death. I told her that she was the most important woman in my life. Those early days were a combination of joy and despair. The joy was in meeting up after being apart. The despair coincided with the length of time that we were apart, even though now I can see that those times weren't really that long. They just felt so long when we were stuck in our respective jobs, both doing awkward shift work with me up in the city whilst Elaine was still down in Binfield.

Elaine quit full-time nursing in the autumn after Mum died and she started a course in Public Administration which she really enjoyed. That eventually helped her to obtain work for an inner-city council organising all their various committees that took place in the evenings. It meant that we didn't see much of each other and gradually our mutual interests waned. I knew that it was the beginning of the end when she told me that she was leaving me behind. And finally, I knew it was over when she couldn't answer my question as to whether she still loved me.

'... *She had a great compassion for people and she got on and did things. I think that I was just a bit too lazy for her and that I didn't really fit into her plans once she started making headway in her new job with the council. She was focused whereas I was wayward, distracted and didn't take the world of work that seriously. My work was just a means to an end for me, though I was interested in the world of mental health, or mental ill-health, as it should really be called.*

I found it hard to manage Elaine's retreat from me, the emotional withdrawal. In a way, I think it related to the loss I'd already known. And I couldn't take the uncertainty of her wavering regard for me. So, I withdrew too in order to protect myself. And we separated a few months later although we did maintain a friendship for a while. I told Tommo all this and he reflected that I found it difficult to manage situations of uncertainty and doubt. I think that he was right. I still miss Elaine and I wonder what she's up to these days. I really should have tried harder. Maybe I'm just not suited to being in a relationship. 'They' say that you've got to work at it. And I've been a bit of a slacker for quite some time. So, this one's going out to dear Elaine, Cap. You'll remember it on the always interesting Harvest label from back in 1973, here featuring the marvellous multi-instrumentalist Roy Wood...'

76

Come What May

'This unlikely record by Vicky Leandros always reminds me of my mum. I guess that I'm lucky to have had her around for the time that I did, Cap. I know that you didn't know your mum and I suspect that was a very tough one for you, but we never really got to talk about that. I guess those chats just didn't happen when we were young back in those days. Well, my mum died in the spring of 1985, just under six years after you went missing. As my auntie Jeanie later said, Mum was going to leave hospital that morning come what may. Mum gave me the money to buy this record for her after the Eurovision Song Contest back in '72 and it was hugely embarrassing to have to go into Guy Norris Records and request it. I'm sure the long-haired fella behind the counter didn't believe me when I told him that it was for my mum.'

I was due to be there at home for Mum when she was due home on that last Monday in April. Unfortunately, she had a bad relapse of her angina and she was very unwell over the week-end before. She rallied, amazingly, on the Sunday and asked me, 'I will be coming home tomorrow, Luggy, won't I?'

All I could say was, 'We'll just have to wait and see tomorrow, Mum.'

And I recall that it was ten to seven on that Monday morning when there was a rousing knock on Elaine's door at the nurses' home. A female voice from behind the door said, 'Phone call for Lugwin'. I knew what it would be about even before I trudged down the stairs to pick up the receiver that was lying off the hook on a metal shelf.

Jack was on the end of the line and he said, 'She's gone.'

Although I'd been told by a young male doctor on the Friday night that 'it could be years, months, weeks, days, hours or even minutes' when she might die, it still felt unreal. I was in a daze as I struggled to put on my socks and shoes. It was a lovely sunny morning as I waited for the cab to take me back to Beastwood, where Jack was waiting for me.

'And I saw that she still had this record, on the blue MGM label, when I was going through some of her possessions prior to leaving her bungalow for the last time. Maybe I should have kept it as a reminder of that record shop embarrassment but it joined her clothes for the charity shop delivery.'

75

Our House

'The repercussions of Mum's death extended to a rift in our family that's never been healed, Cap. You'll recall my brothers were totally different personalities, perchance? The evening following Mum's funeral, the three of us went together to The Bell House, that pub in Beastwood where you and Louise met me in the beer garden shortly after you started going out together. It was a tense affair as Luke started a discussion about what we should do about Mum's bungalow. Ted was off the scene by then having started a relationship with another woman on the quiet. That certainly added to Mum's upsets in that year before her death...'

Luke was hunched over the table and placed his knuckles on his thighs. He said, 'I think that we should keep it on so that we've all got a base for when we want to come back here.'

Jack maintained his impassive expression as he ventured, 'It's going to take money to maintain, which may not be worthwhile with all of us living away from here now. Also, it will be at risk of squatters if it's unoccupied for long periods. I think we should sell up.'

Luke turned to me and asked, 'What about you, Lug?'

'Well, it's going to be difficult for me to afford rent up in the city and contribute to keeping the place ticking over for the occasional times when we might return. I vote we let it go.'

'... and the conversation centred on the pros and cons of keeping Mum's home on. Luke was in a minority for wanting to keep it, on the basis that we'd still have roots in Binfield seeing as we all lived away now. On reflection, he may have been right, but at the time I could only see expenses that I couldn't meet whereas Jack saw threats from potential squatters as it would be unoccupied for most of the time. Not that Beastwood was a hot bed of collective housing action, but Jack was always on the look-out for adverse economic scenarios. It led to Luke becoming estranged from us. He did keep in touch initially with Jack via an address over on Coney Island until all the legal stuff was resolved following the sale of the bungalow and that was it, no more contact after that. I don't know whether he's still over there or not. Jack said that Luke had got a job teaching English as a second language to the Albanian refugees on the Island. I hope he's ok as he's another big person in my life who I miss.

My auntie Jeanie was also right when she said that when you lose the mother in a family, you lose its centre. I guess that could sound simplistic or even sexist these days but I know that it was true for us. Mum held us together when she was there. And like the lead singer of Madness, Suggs, sings so succinctly here, she really is the one we've missed in lots of ways.'

74

My Name Is Jack

My brother Jack was named after my dad. I often think of Jack as the keeper of the family flame due to all the family memorabilia that he has stored since the sale of Mum's home, including an old cine film that he arranged to be recorded onto a video tape. There's footage of him on it as a young boy, looking about my age when Dad died. I was just eight years old then. Jack's standing with Dad outside the front of the old house looking into the fishponds there. He's got one foot up on the little wall surrounding the fishpond and he's sporting his curly brown bouffant and school short trousers. He looked studious even then. He seems to be hanging on Dad's every word. The old cine film medium didn't have any sound on it unfortunately and I'd have loved to have heard my dad speak. I really wish I could remember more clearly what his voice sounded like. I think it must have been a quiet one as I don't have any memory of him raising his voice in the house. He was an undemonstrative man but he conveyed a significant presence.

Dad was the second oldest brother amongst the eight

sons of his parents. His older brother Jimmy was traumatised by his experiences in World War Two and he kept out of public view as far as he could due to his 'nerves'. When my auntie Vera came over for the football coupons on Thursday nights, I'd pop out to see uncle Jimmy, who was waiting in their car, and try to have a chat with him. He was a bit shy and nervous and that was the first time that I'd seen vulnerability close up in an adult. And, of course, I don't think the word 'traumatised' was used then, so I've probably imposed that on Jimmy's wartime experiences. I'd have a very short chat with Jimmy and end up going back inside soon afterwards as apart from telling him what I'd got up to, usually a story about my footballing success, we didn't have a lot to say. He seemed a nice man though. As were most of my dad's brothers. I say 'most' as there were two who I didn't get to know. They came to his funeral but I may or may not have spoken to them. It all seems such a blur. My memory for that sad time back in late '68 is quite patchy. Maybe I'd been traumatised too.

'I think of pop music as really taking off in the sixties, Cap. I know rock 'n' roll and all the crooners were big in the fifties but records such as this seem so steeped in the sixties. This one is from my personal watershed year of 1968, the year that my dad died. He was fifty years old, having been born just a couple of days before the First Great War ended. It was a heart attack or 'a coronary', as I remember Mum calling it. Dad collapsed in the toilet behind me just as I was trying to have a pee. I still have difficulties going in public loos even now. Dad's name was Jack too, so here's Manfred Mann and his talented band playing this Our Tune, for Jack and Jack...'

82

73

My Friend George

'**I** only knew one of my grandparents, Cap, and she was my nan on Mum's side. She died in December, 1975. I didn't want to go to her funeral as I thought it would be a bad memory of Dad's one. I was fifteen by then so Mum allowed me to make up my own mind about it. I remember that Luke was unimpressed by that. We also had some five-a-side football going on at school on that afternoon just after the Christmas holiday and I didn't want to miss it. I guess I was wrong really and I regret it now. This 'Our Tune' though is about another grandparent and that's Donna's grandad, George...'

I first met George back in 1992, the time that Donna took me over to his place to meet him and his little York-shire terrier, Mutt. George must have been about eighty by then. He was still able to get out and about, though Mutt could be a bit too eager for him on those walks. He was a short guy, probably five-foot-six at most, but he had a steely side to him, and a cracking sense of humour too. I used to take him to football matches south of the river Binway, usually lower League or non-League ones where the crowds wouldn't be too much for him on the way in or out, to and from my car. We were able to get to games for most of that season until the spring of '93 when he got the cancer.

Donna was devastated. She loved George. They had a special relationship, that 'plus one generation' relationship that is special between some grandparents and their grandchildren, though that didn't apply in my case. Ah, now I remember another reason why I didn't go to my nan's funeral. When I was very young, about six years old, there'd been a big argument between my mum and one of her sisters, auntie Molly, at my nan's house. I hadn't seen much of my nan after that and I didn't have those special affinities with her that Luke had. But Donna spent as much time as she could with George whilst he was in hospital. He'd decided that he wouldn't have any of that invasive treatment and it was only a couple of months later before he died, in a hospice with lovely staff who even allowed his beloved Mutt to visit him.

'... and it was only on his death, six years ago now, that I was reminded of real grief. I hadn't seen that since after my dad's death and the effect that it had on my mum. Tommo, the psychiatrist at SPiBU, thought that I'd not grieved properly after the various losses of my own during all these years and he thought the culmination of them, the change in my living situation with the move to Donna's place in Harbour Head, the stress of my work with the children and their families, the ongoing uncertainty about what I was going to do with longer-term work down here, and the loss of my old friends from back 'up country' being nearby as a 'support structure', led to this depression that put me in SPiBU for nearly three

months. I still think of George and also of Donna's sunken eyes when we left the hospice that last time. So, this one, by the great Lou Reed, is for my old friend George... '

72

Paradise

'It's time for the 'best local band in the world', Cap, as I remember Dr. Feelgood used to be called. Did you know that their original guitarist and songwriter, Wilko Johnson, was a classmate of our very own English teacher, the Mentor? And do you remember that Wilko used to live opposite the Thomas twins down at the Southbound Grove end of Binfield Valley Drive, in one of those semis that overlooked the tennis courts? Even when he was walking up BVD, he'd always be dressed in that trademark black suit, shirt, tie and boots that we never saw him out of. I've always admired Wilko's singular drive and style, and the resilience that has kept him going in his post-Feelgoods career.

This Wilko-penned track drove a wedge between him and the band but it still ended up on his last album with them, 'Sneakin' Suspicion', released in the early summer of 1977. I'm pleased that it did. It's a great track, with Wilko on lead vocal too, and I love its lines about a thousand highways, not living twice and there being only one road to paradise.

I have this notion now, Cap, of Binfield Valley Drive as my own idealised road. It was the road that took us to Binfield

Hall and also to the tennis courts and the brook. It was the gateway to Binfield Valley Gardens and the home of the Robinson sisters. I remember it as a magical place. It was the road too that I walked down to Southbound Grove in order to get the number 29 bus into Binfield town centre to buy the records which lit up my imagination. I know that the clue is in the word 'idealised' and that BVD has taken on this halcyon hue due to its representation of the joyous aspects of our childhood. I suspect that it wouldn't have this effect on me if I ever returned there. And maybe we have to leave the idealised memories intact and not confront them with the harsher realities of today. But despite that possibility, I would like to go back one day. And I'd like it even more if you could be there with me.'

71

Everyday I Write The Book

'It's the last 'Our Tune', Cap, and it's going out to Andy Griffiths, the occupational therapist who helped me on my discharge from SPiBU. Tommo had arranged for me to see Andy in the Out Patients' Clinic of Helstown Medical Centre. That was in the nearest town to Harbour Head, about a couple of miles or so inland from the coast. An interesting question that Andy asked me in our first meeting was about my relationship with Donna. This got me thinking that there might have been something said concerning the ward round discussions that Donna participated in and when she tried to muscle in about what therapy I might have. She was a domineering force and Andy's angle was whether I might be subsumed by whatever Donna's whims were at any given time. It was a fair assessment, particularly when I was feeling under par with the depression.

The issue that I could deal with though was in giving up the Child Protection work as that was not doing me any favours. I could still get by due to renting out my flat in the city and also look for something less stressful whilst I was convalescing from my time in SPiBU.

Andy had also asked me if I had any interests that I might wish to pursue and of course, the music came up, and a desire to try my hand at a bit of writing. He was very much a 'can do' and 'why not?' type of guy and he suggested that I write a few things about the music. On a daily basis. Some of it has emerged here already. I had let it drift after Andy was no longer overseeing my welfare anymore following the end of the 'Management of Anxiety and Depression' group that I was part of until last year. But he did set me off on starting a musical memoir which I resumed following the split with Donna. And now, from 1983, and with thanks to Andy's promptings, it's time to play Elvis Costello and The Attractions...'

NEWS EAT,
with Laurie Male

News Eat was a weekday fifteen-minute lunch-time show that was aired on *Radio Fun* between quarter to one and one o' clock. It was presented by an upbeat broadcaster by the name of Laurie Male. I'd only really get to hear Laurie's show when I was off school. His news features always had a positive feel to them compared to the dowdy hourly news slots that punctuated the other shows.

70

In The Neighborhood

'**T**hought I'd tag a few news developments on in the latter stages of this C-90, Cap, just to prepare you for the unfurling of more recent developments here in Harbour Head. But before I do, I'd just like to take you back to the late-1980s, when I'd just emerged from the tube station at Booting Broadway. I spotted a familiar figure coming towards me. Six-foot-four, striding along, the swinging shoulders that I remembered from when he approached any prospective dance partner on the Bembridge... yes, you guessed it, it's him... Ben Trippier. Ben was quite myopic so I saw him a little while before he saw me. I deliberately got in the path of his stride and it was only when I stopped his flow that he recognised me. It turned out that Ben was living in the neighbourhood too. I was astonished to learn that he'd become a builder as, to my recollection, Ben was the second least practical man in the world after me...'*

It had been over three years since I last saw Ben. He'd come to my Mum's funeral back in May, 1985. I was pleased to see him but I'd become wary of getting too involved in his shenanigans as they could lead to unnecessary scrapes and unwanted dramas. Not least his chasing of women, be they attached or not, and in the case of the former, he sometimes had to deal with the angry cuckolds. We swapped numbers and arranged to meet up. It was in a big barn of a pub called The Wheatsheaf, opposite Booting tube station. We only met the once. I found that we had less in common than we used to have and I became bemused with Ben's constant ogling of the few women in the pub that night. Just before I left Booting though, after me and Elaine had split up, I gave Elaine Ben's number as she needed some work doing on her flat. In my efforts to keep relations good between us, I hadn't really thought about where that action might lead.

'... *but he was able to help Elaine with various repairs she needed doing in the flat that she moved to, near the Common. Elaine gave him my address down in Harbour Head after Ben found out that I'd moved here and a few years later, he was in my neighbourhood once again. I'll expand on that in a while but in the interim, it's time for Tom Waits...*'

69

A New Career In A New Town

'Elaine moved again, Cap, closer to Binfield. She kept her flat on in Booting though she was undecided about her longer-term plans. She rented it out and moved into a nurses' home at Speedwell hospital so she could undertake training to become a psychiatric nurse. She'd had enough of the late-night council committees and she wanted to work with people at the 'sharp end' again. She also thought that being 'dual-trained' might be helpful in getting into nursing management eventually. We kept the channels of communication open for as long as possible. But when I realised that Donna liked me as more than a friend, well, it was difficult to keep seeing Elaine because of how Donna felt about that. In fact, Donna wanted me to press ahead with a divorce so that she knew I didn't harbour any plans for a reconciliation with Elaine. I did that. It felt a bit brutal but I respected Donna's wishes first. Anyway, I received a nice letter from Elaine in the Christmas period just after I moved to Harbour Head. I'll read it to you: -

Dear Lug,

I hope that you're settling into your new home and that life down there is all you want it to be. I thought it was brave of you to 'up sticks' to such a far-flung part of the country but I've heard that it's lovely and here's wishing you well in your new job too. Talking of which, I'm loving psyche nursing — it's a whole different world to general nursing and it really keeps me on my toes!

I've made some friends in my student group and they're good fun. They're quite a mix of ages and backgrounds and it feels a very positive move to be out of the city as I didn't really connect with that many people there. It might still be useful to keep the flat on for work in the future though. I'll have to wait and see.

Anyway, I hope this letter doesn't get you in trouble with Donna. I know that you need to minimise our future contact but I just wanted to wish you all the very best from 'out east' and to let you know that I still value your friendship and I would welcome any contact from you if this won't cause you any problems.

Love and thoughts,

Elaine xx

Donna wasn't back from one of her overnight shifts when I received that letter so luckily, I didn't face an enquiry about who it was from. I was chuffed to receive it. It felt like though our marriage had been a failure, our friendship was still very much intact.

'I was really pleased to hear it was working out well for Elaine. I knew Speedwell too. My mum had worked in the patients' shop there for a few years before she died. Mum loved it. She got me a job there that summer when you went missing. It was a cleaning job. I wasn't very good but I did become a nursing assistant there the following year in the college holidays. It was hard work but I enjoyed it. That experience prompted me to start psychiatric nurse training myself back in the summer of '82. That's another story for another time though. In the mean-time, Cap, here's a track from one of my favourite albums, David Bowie's 'Low'. It's also the B-side to that wonderful single 'Sound and Vision'...'

68

Donna

'It was on New Year's Day of this year, Cap. I'm not sure
when you'll get this broadcast exactly but that was just over
a couple of months ago now. I was down in the studio area
below deck, and amongst the decks, where I was writing a bit
of this memoir. It's good down here. It's peaceful and whenever
I look up, I've got a good view through the portholes where I
can see several aspects of the harbour. And then, late morning,
close to noon, I noticed her. She was wearing her long black
leather coat and she was walking towards the ship. Well, I call
it a ship, but it's a big boat – or a diving vessel, as the Producer
told me. She looked quite pale as she got nearer. She stopped to
inspect The Southern Star. I decided to go up on deck and
announce myself just in case she was trying to find the best way
on board...'

'Hi Donna. Happy new ninety-nine.'

'Ah, there you are. Happy new year, Lug. You alright?'

'Yeah, a few cobwebs from being up at the Atlantic late
last night and into the early hours, but otherwise fine. And
you? Come on up if you like.'

'Thanks. Yeah, okay. I will.'

I put the gangplank out to the harbourside and held out my hand for her as she neared its summit. She took it. Her hand was cold. Or 'taties', to use her own description.

'Hey – warm hand there, Loggie! Thank you.'

It was nice to hear that affectionate nick-name from our happier times.

So, she came aboard The Southern Star and was quite taken with its quirky features. She commented on my music posters that she hadn't allowed me to put up in Homely and gave Oscar lots of cuddles. That made me wish for that kind of affection again.

Funnily enough, the Producer had only said last night up at the pub how much more relaxed I was these days. He felt that I was always a bit on tenterhooks when I was with Donna. I think that I was wary of her volatile moods and her need to be the centre of attention. I noted that she always went very quiet and appeared to be thinking of something else whenever the conversation with other people didn't revolve around her chosen topics. It was quite a powerful tool of letting others know that she was disinterested until another subject emerged upon which she might vent her forthright opinion.

But she surprised me on that unexpected visit, Cap. It turned out that she'd been missing me. We'd split up nearly two months before. She had been reconsidering things, she said. She said that maybe she had acted too hastily. She suggested that maybe, if I felt the same, that we might 'go out together again'. I was quite taken aback. I had got used to this new way… ah, I was going to say 'this new way of being' but pulled myself up just in time… this new lifestyle which I was very much enjoying. However, without dwelling too long on it so that it looked ambivalent, I said something like 'yeah, sure, why not?' but I didn't actually ring her in the following weeks to arrange anything. It was good to spend some time with her again before she left though.

She also told me that she'd picked up a message on the answerphone for me 'about a bloke called Ben who wished you a happy new year and who said he's planning to come down and see you.' I told her about how I hadn't seen Ben in a few years and how I wanted to keep it that way. I asked her not to tell him where I was if he rang again. I know it sounds a bit harsh, Cap, but having had the therapy in recent years, it taught me not to be doing with any people who might make life more difficult for me. I felt that Ben might bring some trouble to my gradually happier state that was evolving and I wanted to keep my life as trouble-free as possible. And the same went for Donna too.

So, without any further ado, here's 10cc. I'm sorry, Donna, I didn't mean to keep you waiting by the telephone. But things are getting better for me now and I would prefer to keep it this way.'

67

Wavelength

'**T**he Producer loved it when I first told him about our imaginary radio station, Cap, and how back in the days of our home recordings, we hoped that everyone in my household would keep quiet whilst we recorded our shows. He suggested that I should re-enact my moniker from those times as *The Emperor*, who I based on that crazy jock from across the Atlantic, *Emperor Boss Co.*, as I loved his shows on *Radio Fun* on Saturday mornings. So here I am as 'the Emperor Luggo' on my show *Radio Binfield* which goes out on a daily basis from our studio at *The Southern Star*. And the Producer's been busy with an application to the State Casino funding guys, *Jackpot*, with a view to getting our community radio station on a national wavelength. He's got to present it to a panel of assessors next month so it's all go around here. He wants to get us one of those prized waveband slots that are allocated to the community radio stations and also to augment our shows, currently his *Drivetime* slot on the post-school and work runs and my *Breakfast Show*, with more daytime slots featuring other presenters who he's currently training.

It's been really busy here lately but Oscar's been enjoying the extra company. He's been particularly aroused by one of the new female jocks in training, a chatty and charming local woman called Katie. Katie always spends time talking to him and giving him some hearty strokes. I like her, Cap, and it's good to meet new people through this nascent station. I realise that I'm very lucky in having met the Producer too. He's really helped me to bounce back from being despatched from Homely to a berth here where I feel much more at home. A re-birth, if you'll excuse the pun. I really hope that he can get the Jackpot gang on side to make his dreams happen. He really deserves it and I'm so proud to be part of it too.

And on that note, and hoping for the best, here's Van Morrison with the title track of his album 'Wavelength' which came out in 1978...'

66

I'm Coming Out

'**I**'m guessing that you may not have expected to hear this track from Diana Ross on one of my broadcasts, Cap, but it's here due to some recent correspondence that I received from out east. Just before Christmas, all the cards that I sent out were for the purpose of informing the few people who I wanted contact from in the future as to where I'd moved to. The Producer hasn't got a phone set up here and I'm not particularly wishing to carry around one of those hideous mobile gadgets as I don't like being at the beck and call of the world out there. So, anyone who wants to contact me has to do so by letter – especially as I'm not 'on line' either. I know it sounds a bit dinosaur, but I like it that way.

And Scotchy rose to my communication challenge. He's been letting people know what we've all known for some time but didn't want to acknowledge until he felt the time was right. He went back to Binfield just after Christmas and told his family first. Brother Pete was there and had some news of his own, that he visited you in Speedwell just before Christmas. I'm sorry to hear that you've been through the mental ill-health system yourself, Cap, but it's good to hear, even third-hand, *that you're alive and almost well.*

I hope that you're on the road to recovery and I'm going to send you these first two broadcasts from the earlier part of the day to Speedwell in the hope that they get to you soon. I hope they will be welcome and that you might enjoy this unusual way of catching up. I also hope that you've got a Walkman there so you can hear them in private if you're still an in-patient on the ward. I'll be working on the afternoon shows soon and I would be delighted if you could send me your address so I can ensure that they get to you ok when I've completed them.

Take good care, my old friend, and all the very best from way out west. So, let's finish off this broadcast with this single from 1980 and let's raise a glass of the orange stuff to dear old Scotchy too...'

SOVILE'S TRAVAILS,
with Jimmy Sovile

Probably the most famous disc jockey and a ubiquitous face on TV when I was growing up was Jimmy Sovile. He was a 'larger than life' character. I didn't particularly like him or his shows but he was very hard to ignore.

65

On The Run

'**G**reetings once again, Cap! Thought I'd go a little bit away from the normal week-day schedule of Radio Fun with this particular segment, just because of the coincident theme of mental illness that I spoke about in the last broadcast.

You'll remember that 'Sovile's Travails' used to go out on a Sunday lunch-time and featured that well-known, self-aggrandising jock, Jimmy Sovile, who used to run marathons for charity and do voluntary work at various hospitals around the country. Well, I actually saw him once fairly close-up at Binmoor Secure Hospital in early '83. He had turned up to start the Inter-Psychiatric Hospitals Cross-Country Race that year and I was part of the team for the hospital that I was working in, Binchley Hatch. Jimmy was having a bit of a set-to with one of our runners, Tony, and he got a bit heated...'

Tony had been provocative to the bleach-blond haired man who became Sir Jim. I could make out their exchange as I was only about three metres away. Let me take you back to that cold and grey afternoon of late January, 1983.

'You're a bit of a wanker really, aren't you Jimmy?'

Jimmy took his cigar out of his mouth and retorted

immediately, 'I'll tell you who the wanker is. The wanker is you and people like you who have to work for a living.'

Jimmy then went on about how he doesn't have to work and how he's only here because he gives his time and effort voluntarily to good causes. Although Tony had lit the fuse, it revealed an interesting insight into this much-loved celebrity's way of thinking.

'... and though he had the last word, it left me thinking how the image had cracked and that there was definitely another side to him beyond his charismatic TV and radio persona. So, I'm going to tell you a little about my experience and how I had to adopt a different persona in order to fulfil my work duties. Hearing that you've been staying in Speedwell lately also made it more poignant. And I guess that I can chart my own experience of personal mental health concerns back to before I started out doing that psychiatric nurse training at Binchley Hatch, just north of the city's North Circular Road, back in the summer of '82.

I'd experienced shades of depression – but nothing deemed as clinical – in my teens, Cap. I guess all teenagers have a little bit of that at times but they try hard not to show it to their peers. When I was at college, I'd also started to experience what I thought of as feelings of dissociation, where I felt somewhat out of touch with my surroundings. I never had much warning of it but it left me with a sense that the real world wasn't that real at all and that all of our activity was seemingly futile. Some aspects of life really didn't seem to matter to me and it all felt like a pointless TV show happening beyond my own world. It was a strange but sometimes liberating place to be. I carried on trying to act 'normal' as I knew that it would sound weird to anyone if I talked about this kind of stuff. Another trait I felt that I had which was outside of the so-called normal range was in the varying moods that I had. I wouldn't describe them as full blown 'manic-depression' which was the label at the time, but they were definitely 'cyclothymic', a milder version of this.

And that was another reason for dipping my toe into the world of psychiatry. Not only did I need to obtain some more secure accommodation after the flat in Rectory Grove got condemned following one too many train-rush shudders, I was also keen to know more about my own increasingly brittle mental health. I figured, quite rationally at that time, that I could achieve both of these objectives by living in a nurses' home whilst doing this training.

I hope that you're sitting comfortably as I'll tell you some more after this track. It's by Eddie and The Hot Rods and it alludes to mental illness. It's from their debut album, 'Teenage Depression'. And I think that, akin to the lyrics of this one, I've been on the run for some time. On the run from mental illness, of course. But, as the saying goes, you can run but you can't hide.

64

Solitary Confinement

Room 104 in Coleman House measured about ten by seven feet. It was what an estate agent might describe as 'comfortably-sized' for someone's spare bedroom. It was my room in the nurses' home of Binchley Hatch for just over three years. Most of the other residents nearby were either established nursing or domestic staff and they generally kept to themselves. I had to take care to have my music on softly or listen through the cans because of the various shifts that we were all doing.

I wasn't a natural in the world of psychiatric nursing. Though I was a good listener, I was a bit awkward with the practical stuff and as I've got older, I've thought that I might have a mild form of dyspraxia due to certain difficulties that I have with remembering the sequence of some tasks. I just about got by, though one charge nurse did suggest on my student nurse report that I would benefit from counselling as to whether this was the right path for me. I think that she was right. I certainly struggled with 'the institution versus the individual' issues that occur in such places.

'This one, Cap, is the first single that I heard by The Members. It was in late '78 and was released on Stiff Records and had a red label. I was up in the old attic room in Beastwood and I was feeling a bit down about the A levels that we were doing at the time. It all felt a bit much for me and, as you know, I was struggling at Pouk Hill. You kept encouraging me though. And the grades that I eventually got were just enough to get me into a Poly in the city shortly after you went missing. I lived in small rooms playing my records for the next few years. A shuddering box room in Rectory Grove, then a slightly larger one in the nurses' home at Binchley Hatch. I used to think that it was like living in solitary confinement but of course it wasn't. The music provided me with the freedom of imagination that I lacked in whatever I was doing in the real world. And the power of the radio to turn me onto records like this – ones that really spoke to me – never ceases to inspire me, though I'm not hearing so many of them these days that I used to, sadly.

I remember you used to say how the best music can take you through the bad times as well as the good times. Well, this was one that helped me through the bad times. I found it pretty difficult at Binchley Hatch. I remember working on an acute admissions unit where the charge nurse had a 'locked door' policy as she'd had to stand up in a Coroner's Court and answer questions about a patient who'd left the ward and hung himself in the woods at the far end of the hospital grounds. I was escorting this young guy – about my age then, 22 years old – from one of the open, unlocked wards to the ward that I was working on and when I unlocked the door and waited for him to go in, he turned to me and said, 'You're *not locking me in, are you?' and I had to say, 'Only temporarily. People can go out but we need to check how you are each time before you do.' I could see the shock on his face, Cap. It really seemed like a throw-back to a bygone age. I had to swallow a lot of my liberal beliefs in order to get by there and I did find it very uncomfortable. I'm surprised that I lasted there for over three years. But a sunny Saturday one September changed all that...'*

63

Where Have All The Good Times Gone?

I knew something wasn't quite right that morning when I'd been trying to wash an elderly man in a 'bed bath' with a fellow student and friend, Ian. Ian had to take the lead as I'd suddenly become a bit vague and lost all sense of what needed to be done. I felt a bit helpless and a lot hapless. It was a strange feeling. When I got back to Room 104 after the shift, I just slumped into bed and I didn't get up for several hours.

'It was a lovely day, Cap. Usually after a morning shift, I'd have been keen to get out there and do something. Maybe go and watch some football in the local park or head off into town and have a look in the record shops. But not that Saturday afternoon. I just stayed in bed and worried about what was happening to me. I'd lost all sense of myself. It all seemed so pointless. I thought that this might be a proper depression creeping up on me. It was coming up to five months after Mum died. I was really missing Elaine too. I'd come to find it very hard being apart from her now. Also, I knew that I wasn't cut out for the nursing. I just had to hang on in there to complete the exam and then I'd leave. I didn't owe anyone there

anything. I could also get by on the money that I'd come into after Mum's death. Twenty-five grand was a lot back then. About four times what I was getting paid on the student nurse income over the year. And there'd be more to come when we sold Mum's place too. She'd not want me to stay doing something that was not doing me any good, surely?...'

When I did get up to use the loo, sometime around six or seven that evening, I just went straight back to bed afterwards. I didn't want to see anyone and I certainly didn't want anyone to see me in this state either. I decided that I'd go as soon as I took the nursing exam. I'd pack up everything in my room and see when Jack could help me get it all back to Mum's bungalow in Beastwood. And then I'd stay there until I could work out my next move.

'So, I jacked it in on the following Wednesday, Cap. I had my resignation letter already to plonk in the reception of the Nurse Education Centre when I came out of the exam. I'd paid my rent up 'til the end of the month so I was still in front by the week-end when Jack came down from Spiresville and helped me to get all my records and gear into his car for the journey back to Beastwood. Mum's bungalow hadn't been sold by then but it was just a matter of time. I felt a whole lot better as soon as I'd said goodbye to Binchley Hatch. I didn't realise just how much it had affected me. Elaine said she'd never seen me as relaxed as I was just after I left there. It was good to be out of the madhouse, Cap. Even if I wasn't able to stay out of there for too long. And now it's time for The Kinks to remind us of those feelings of desolation...'

62

Ghosts

I'd definitely recommend getting out of a situation if it's compromising your health. I was lucky to be in a position to do so. I'd been the beneficiary of money locked away since my dad's death and when Mum died, it came my way. I think that if I hadn't had that nest egg to fall back on, then I'd have sunk further into depression at Binchley Hatch and who knows, I may even have been admitted there eventually. But, at that time, I got away with it. I still felt low and lacking in self-esteem even though I'd escaped the place. I had to consider what I could do which wouldn't cause me stress through not being up to the job.

The time that I had back in Beastwood gave me the space to evaluate things before I had to move on. Elaine, too, was on the cusp of changing her own direction and that's when she'd signed up for the course in Public Administration. So, my return to Beastwood provided her with some temporary accommodation too when she had to leave the nurses' home in Binfield later that month. It all worked out just right even though they were hastily planned decisions. We had the time together that I'd been longing for and I was free from most of the anxiety that I experienced every day and increasingly overnight in those last weeks at Binchley Hatch.

'Despite being relieved to be out of the asylum, Cap, it was weird being back in Mum's place. It was a bit like some of the sentiments in that song by The Jam, 'Ghosts'. I felt that I'd lost part of myself being in a situation that I wasn't suited to and became increasingly frightened of the future, wondering whether there was anything that I might be able to do now. Even if you've walked away from a stressful situation voluntarily, there's always that feeling that you've failed. And obviously, Mum's place was now so much sadder without her being there. Elaine lived with me there for a few months before we had to move once it was sold early in the new year of 1986. There were ghosts all around for me at that time, Cap. Still no contact from my brother Luke. And, of course, it was strange being back in Binfield without you around too. But I hope that we can change that one of these days.'

61

Caravan Man

'*I wonder if you might recall Johnny Green from Pouk Hill, Cap? Better known as 'Hippy' Johnny amongst our peers. Tall, sporting long flaxen hair, a toothy smile emanating from his reddish face, and a perpetual wearer of desert boots. Usually he'd be seen with a Grateful Dead album under his arm when walking around those terracotta-tiled quadrangles that looked out towards the school's impenetrable gardens. A nice guy and a defiant bastion of the 'counter-culture' when punk rock and the 'new wave' reared their unwelcome heads in his musical universe in the last years of our time at that place.'*

That time in late 1985 when me and Elaine lived together in Beastwood was a process of discovery for me. I'd never really explored anywhere that I couldn't get to by bus as I found when I started to learn to drive in '79 that I still had a lot of anxiety from that car accident back when I was a kid. So, I gave that up. A familiar theme. However, Elaine did drive and she took me to a few places out in the sticks. One of them was Binford, where I was actually born. It's a small town about two miles north-east of Beastwood and about three miles north-west of Binfield. However, it had a hospital there where Elaine had done some of her nursing training. It had several general nursing wards, a psychiatric unit and a maternity unit, where I'd been born twenty-five years previously. I'd never spent any time in Binford whilst growing up though and Elaine wanted to change that. She thought I'd like a pub there that she used to go to when she was a student nurse. And she was right: the Golden Lion, with its timber-fronted panels and sparse interior, was a fantastic old-fashioned pub of the type that I adore.

I ran into him again when Elaine and I were on a night out at the Golden Lion in Binford. I recognised him as he loped in. He was sporting the double denim look and he still wore desert boots. After he got his pint, he sat down in the corner away from us and read his newspaper, intermittently puffing on a roll-up. He clocked me eventually and came over after he got his second pint. I did the introductions, he sat with us and we did the catch-up stuff. He was working as a handyman and gardener at a local care home and was living in his caravan, which he was able to park in the grounds of the home.

Johnny was interested in the fact that I'd been training to be a psychiatric nurse and that Elaine was already qualified as a general nurse. He said there were vacancies at the care home and asked if we might be interested. I was still in a bit of a daze post-Binchley Hatch, so I told him that I needed a bit of 'time out' currently. However, Elaine was interested in the possibility of doing a few shifts to complement her student grant.

It turned out that Dave Paynter had a share in the company that ran the home. He'd become a nurse himself after his brother Graham had died from a drug overdose. I'd actually seen Graham in my last year at City Poly back in '82. Graham was looking pale and rough back then. Very thin and lots of scabs on his face. He was also a bit distracted. I thought something wasn't quite right. And from what Johnny said, it seemed like Dave had changed a lot and wanted to do something worthwhile with his life. We laughed about how Dave used to drone on in that sixth-form common room, the Hardon Room, about the dictatorship of the proletariat, and how he got nick-named 'Spart' after the polemicist called Dave Spart in that satirical magazine, Public Eye. Well, it turns out that Spart's private grief had helped to transform him into a caring entrepreneur.

But that was a great chance meeting with Johnny as when Elaine and I had to leave my mum's place, she was able to live in the 'on-call' room at the care home so long as she could be available for any nocturnal emergencies or urgent advice to the night care staff. She got to know Spart too. Turns out that he'd become a really nice guy in these intervening years. I think that he developed his interest in care homes when 'community care' took off.

I needed to make arrangements for myself back in that community when I knew that I couldn't stay in Beastwood for much longer. Hats off to Johnny for being able to manage that cold winter of '85-'86 in his caravan though. And talking of which, here's Lew Lewis on the legendary Stiff Records label...'

60

Winning

'I don't know if you're a fan of The Sound, Cap, but this opening track from their second album, 'From The Lion's Mouth', released in 1981, really hits the spot for me for a time in the mid-80s when things started changing for the better. From drowning to swimming to winning, that's how it was for me in late '85 to early '86. I'd also been able to pick up Sunday morning football again once I quit nursing...'

It was Jack who put me in touch with one of his old friends who'd recently moved to just outside the Old Town. A nice guy by the name of Haydn. He was a social worker in his day job and the player-manager of a football team in the Binstead District League on Sunday mornings. I'd been conscious of the need to be more active as the brush I had with depression had certainly led to me being more slothful and the weight had piled on. And football had always raised my game in that respect. It was one of the few types of exercise that I really enjoyed. Our team suffered heavy defeats on a regular basis. I can only recall us winning once and that lead to an ironic dressing room comment post-match about how 'that result will send shock waves around the Binstead District League', but it was still a joy to be involved in some group activity, collective effort and, of course, the post-match pint. And that's where I met one interesting dude by the name of Padraig Ronan Oscar Vincent MacManus – or 'Prov', for short.

'... and I got a lift up to Binstead Flats, where we played our home games, and various other pitches around the eastern city district for our away games, courtesy of our player-manager, Haydn. He told me how doing voluntary work with Social Services would give me useful experience and help get me back into work eventually. He worked in Bestminster and one of his work-mates came along to our games. A very interesting guy. His name 'Prov' was an acronym of his four forenames. Prov was a touch-typist for Social Services and he was a mine of musical knowledge. I used to crack on with him in the pub after our games. He taught me a lot about how to manage having a disability and I was hugely impressed by his resilience and his strategies of coping with his blindness. He was also a very kind guy. Despite only knowing me a short while, he offered to put me up at his flat shortly before Mum's place was sold. It was in Bestminster and not far from the office where Haydn suggested that I take up the volunteering.'

59

I Can See Clearly Now

That spring of '86 was a good one. I think back to those days and remember most of them as sunny. I'd be walking around my patch in South Bestminster going between the estates and undertaking a variety of roles for the 'Area 3' office under the supervision of Angela, my volunteer organiser. She was there from early in the morning to late at night, a really conscientious person and impressively driven.

I felt that I got my life force back then after being subsumed in a fog of bewilderment and hopelessness in much of the year after Mum died. It was a great suggestion by Haydn and he definitely helped to put me back on track. That experience was valuable and much of what I learnt has stayed with me. It helped me to see what it was like for the stay-at-home public and when I got my big break in radio, I could visualise some of the lives of the listeners and empathise a bit better with their travails. It was a different kind of voluntary work to that of the infamous Jimmy Sovile, the original DJ-cum-charity-mogul and his hospital patronage, but I like to think that it helped to shape my perspectives and provide me with more sensitivity towards people who were socially isolated and struggling to manage. The Producer recognised that quality in me years later and he also handed me another lifeline just when I needed it again.

The volunteer tasks were mostly practical, such as helping people with paying their bills or getting their shopping in but some roles did involve 'social outreach' too, such as trying to encourage depressed older people into leaving their home again or joining them to attend an activity that they might enjoy. I wasn't always successful in achieving those goals but the people who had become housebound due to anxiety did generally appreciate the visits to see how they were doing. I may have been the only person they'd see for days. I found that it generally took a few visits to establish the essential trust involved and then you can build from there, all being well.

And talking of trust, what about the incredibly good Samaritan himself, Prov MacManus? Without him, this re-awakening would not have been possible. He had a one-bedroomed flat in Ebury, a western district of South Best-minster, which was quite a mixed area of relative affluence conjoined with relative deprivation.

Prov was well known in Ebury, having lived there since 1978, and the locals looked out for him. He loved the pubs in the vicinity, particularly the Ebury Arms, which was like a little village inn tucked away in a side-street. I used to meet him there most evenings after doing the voluntary work and he was already ensconced in dialogue with whoever was hanging around the bar.

I admired Prov's confidence and his ability to hold his own in whichever situation he found himself in. He once told me that being blind had helped him to discern people's nature as his listening skills were more enhanced than most people's due to his blindness. He certainly had a laser-like focus in nailing the nub of any issue and working out how he would deal with it. And he could be merciless in noting others' shortcomings when they didn't meet with his own standards or when their behaviour didn't accord with his requirements. You had to watch out for that collapsible cane of his which he'd whack you on the knee with if you pushed it with him. And the locals in the Ebury sure loved seeing him do that.

'So, Jack loaded up his car again with my stuff and took me out to Ebury where I stayed with Prov for a few months before sorting out my own place in Booting. Jack took most of my gear, including my records and my music system back to his home in Spiresville, as there wasn't much room at Prov's.

I slept on a camp bed in Prov's lounge and it worked out well. I remember one time though, when I was really tired and wasn't saying much one late evening, that Prov became uneasy. He thought that I must be down because I wasn't pushing the chat. That was one indication of the differing perceptions that might exist between our different worlds. Also, I needed to be very careful not to move anything from where he'd put it originally as he had a system where he could find things easily, so long as they remained where he'd left them. And another rule was never leave the toilet seat down. He was sometimes in a hurry to get there and he didn't want to fiddle around beforehand and he obviously didn't want any 'splashbacks' either.

I still think of his generosity, Cap – not many people would take you in like that after only knowing you a short while. I like to think that I might have had a good impact on his life too, especially through introducing him to Scotchy during that time. They've been close friends ever since. They're two of the most loveable drinking rogues that I know and they're clearly very well-suited. Haydn reckoned that bringing those two together was the best piece of social work that he'd ever seen.

This one by Johnny Nash, from 1972, is going out to Prov. Though he's blind, he's one of the most discerning people who I know. And his charity certainly began at home. He also helped me to embark on a new path.'

58

Free Range

'It was important to give Prov a bit of space at week-ends, Cap, and I was keen to see Elaine down in Binford too. She had to be available at the care home overnight and so I used to hang out with Hippy Johnny in the Golden Lion on the Saturday evenings. It was Johnny who told me that you might be living out near Coney Island, in that wooded area bordering the Wrestling Fields...'

The Wrestling Fields were so named because of their history as a place where tough men from the neighbouring communities of Binfield and Coney Island used to settle their differences in combat. It was a vast patch of land which separated Binfield – and in particular its Old Town – from Coney Island, which was just across the narrow estuary. The train line from Binfield to the city also ran between Binfield West rail station, just on the western edge of the Old Town, towards Binfleet station, the stop across the estuary from Coney Island. Just north of the train line and south of the Wrestling Fields was a wooded area which had become a temporary home to a few members of a free-range travelling community.

Johnny had some friends over there and one of them, a traveller named Shane, had mentioned to him that there was a guy called Winston who'd settled deep in the wood in a shack that had fallen into a state of disrepair. Bearing in mind that Winston is such an unusual name these days – Wiz had been named by his grandfather who was a big fan of Winston Churchill – and by the description of him given by Shane, it seemed highly likely that it was my missing friend. Shane told Johnny that Winston kept to himself and wouldn't talk to any of the free-rangers unless pressed. It seemed like he resented them coming into his patch. We never did find out for sure whether this Winston was Wiz, but I know Wiz had a dream that he might own a cabin in the wilds one day and he was going to call it *The Captain's Cabin*.

'*... and that reminded me of your vision of living in The Captain's Cabin, away from the numbers and where you could be far from the maddening crowds. If you ever did make it into free-range, off-grid living, then I believe that it's time for The Fall...*'

57

Autonomy

'**I** did want to go over there to see if you had installed yourself in *The Captain's Cabin*, Cap, but Johnny discouraged me on the basis that the travelling folk who were there at the time would have found it unsettling and they may have reacted defensively towards some unannounced interloper in their midst. I was intrigued about your choice of location, if you did make it there.

The only time that I can remember exploring the Wrestling Fields was in one of our Geography field trips from Pouk Hill. That must have been back in the spring of 1973, if I recall correctly. And talking of recall, all I can remember from the geography side of that trip is looking at several stagnant ponds. It was more the view of those oil refineries over on Coney Island in the distance beyond the fields that really shines brightly in my memory though.

They were troubled times over on the island. Although I didn't really understand it back in '73, I discovered later that the Albanian community over there had been protesting about being discriminated against, particularly when it came to obtaining employment on the mainland. The military wing of the Albanian Civil Rights Movement, the Albanian Brigade, were also portrayed as 'terrorists' on the TV news and in the press. That was even before their bombs killed anyone. But about a year after you went missing, the Albanian people of Coney Island won a limited form of self-government in their ongoing struggle for greater autonomy.

I noticed the Albanian language cropping up on the signs at Binfleet rail station from the early eighties too. It was almost as if the Albanians were now seen as accepted following years of second-class citizenship since their first wave of immigration to Coney Island after King Zog had been forced to flee Albania following the invasion of Mussolini's troops in 1939. Fascinating stuff, Cap, and apologies for the history lesson that I'm sure you didn't need, but I've always had a sneaking regard for the Albanian people and their struggles in adversity.

I'll tell you about a visit I paid to the motherland shortly. In the meantime, here's the Buzzcocks.'

56

I'm Just Beginning To Live

'*Just enough time to wrap up this side of the C-90, Cap, with a circular mental health connection, and a track courtesy of Jonathan Richman and The Modern Lovers. The voluntary work in South Bestminster put me in the frame for applying for internal Council vacancies and my manager, Angela, alerted me to one that she thought would be ideal for me. That was the post of a welfare assistant in a Mental Health Project down by the River Binway. It was the first interview that I'd had in a few years, but I'd got my confidence back through doing the volunteering and as I'd got to know the locale quite well in the four months that I'd been doing it, I felt quite good crossing the threshold at the MHP, as we called the Project, particularly as I'd already helped to introduce some of the gang to the drop-in centre there and I knew the type of place it was.*

Those group interviews can be quite revealing. I sat back and listened for most of the time and just contented myself with asking a couple of questions about 'service-user represent- ation' and some of the other buzz-phrase jargon back then. I felt that the staff were giving us clues as to what was required but some people in the interview were just a bit too insistent on proselytising their views about mental health practice to take it all in.

By the time that my individual interview came around in the afternoon, I felt really positive. It was such a progressive place compared to the Victorian asylum that I'd been working in at Binchley Hatch. I think that my enthusiasm shone through when I spoke about learning from prospective experienced colleagues, developing counselling skills, participating in group-work and, of course, hosting the drop-in centre. Larry, who led the interview, rang me up later that afternoon to tell me that I'd got it. I was buzzing. It really seemed like a new start.

Elaine was proud of me too. I was still seeing her in Binford at weekends but after I started the job and sorted out a mortgage a few months later, she was able to give up the sleep-ins at the care home and move in with me at the flat in Booting. She'd also got a student placement arranged with Bestminster Council with the organisation of their committee meetings. It all seemed so good just then. Despite all the difficulties of recent times, it felt just like the songs says and that I was beginning to live again...'

THE EARLY AFTERNOON SHOW,
with Johnnie Talker

Of all the jocks from my youth, my admiration for Johnnie Talker remains immense. However, I only really got to listen to Johnnie's show on Radio Fun in the school holidays or joyously, when off school through being unwell. In those years from 1972 to 1974, in particular, Johnnie regularly introduced me to music that was a little 'off playlist', though I do remember him once hinting that he really wouldn't be playing a Bay City Rollers single if he had any choice in the matter. I loved that slightly coy subversiveness in his delivery. And I am thoroughly enjoying Johnnie's Saturday afternoon shows now on *Radio Snooze* too...'

55

Talent Is An Asset

'**W**elcome back, Cap, to part two of this broadcast. We're now at the stage where we recall one of the finest voices on radio, the magnificent Johnnie Talker. He was one of the original pirates who came back to land who lit up Radio Fun in the early nineteen-seventies. Those years of relative isolation back then during the holidays from Pouk Hill were leavened by Johnnie's shows. I particularly liked his championing of new records that weren't played on the other daytime shows in his 'One to Watch' daily feature over the week and the LP tracks that he selected for his 'Album of the Week' slot.

I distinctly recall him playing a track off 'Kimono My House' by Sparks every day over one week in a school holiday during 1974. It was a gloriously sunny week. I think it must have been in the summer holidays. I know that I rushed out to get it with my paper round money as soon as I could. This one on side two, at track two, was sheer genius, and it always reminds me of our family's resident genius, Jack Junior.

My brother Jack had the brains in our family and he went off to that bastion of establishment learning, Spiresville University, back in the autumn of '71. He must have been revising *for, or sitting, his finals when this came out in May '74. Just like those brothers from Sparks, Ron and Russell Mael of Sparks, my own brothers are an unusual pair. I've learned a lot from both of them though, in their different ways...'*

My brother Luke is nine years older than me and Jack is seven years older. I think that I may have been a Valentine Night's 'accident' due to the age disparity between me and my brothers and because I was born in mid-November.

It was great having older brothers when they were at home as we'd get to play football together indoors and out-doors. The indoor games took place in the kitchen of the old house when Mum was working some evenings in a pub soon after Dad died. There was a rectangular area hollowed out underneath a work surface at one end of the square kitchen which made an ideal goal and the sliding cupboard doors at the opposite end made do for the other goal. I always defended the cupboard end due to the huge thrill of scoring when the little rubber ball pinged into the corners of the work surface goal.

There used to be some good wrestling matches too when Mum was out. Luke always had the upper hand in those bouts and I'd of course join in when Jack was safely subdued. I also remember being frog-marched by Jack to receive justice from Mum when I'd hit him with a tennis racquet. I don't recall why I did such a spiteful thing, but I clearly had a nasty side, even at four years old.

'... and Jack has been a great source of support in recent years when it's all been a bit topsy-turvy for me. Though I don't see him that much these days, he's always steadfast and reassuring whenever we get to chat. He's head of the Economics

*department up at his college in Spiresville now. I doubt that
he's a Sparks fan but this one's going out to our dear talented
Jack...'*

54

Power To The People

'**A**nd Luke was influential too, Cap, due to his zealous championing of the underdog. I'd often find him reading political tracts in his room whilst he was also playing records by the protest singers and music revolutionaries like John Lennon, particularly from that time at the turn of the decade from the sixties to the seventies, when John had formed the Plastic Ono Band. Luke informed me about the plight of the Albanian people and how they'd been discriminated against here on the mainland for decades. I remember that he used to go over to Coney and join in the Civil Rights protests.'

Luke told me in one of our later conversations that he'd been tempted to join the Albanian Brigade before they'd been proscribed and then later suppressed by the mainland state. He was impressed with their direct action and how they shook up the establishment with their 'peaceful' bombing campaign of high society bars, police stations, army barracks and financial institutions. Luke said that there was no other way of bringing about change as the Albanian Civil Rights Movement could only go so far and the state wasn't listening.

Luke used to wear a badge depicting the Albanian flag, with black eagles on a red background, accompanied by the Brigade's slogan, *These outrages must cease.* That was their message each time one of their 'peaceful' bombs went off in reaction to whatever recent injustice they'd felt had been meted out to the Albanian people.

The Albanian Brigade described their bombings as 'peaceful' as they always gave a thirty-minute warning for people to get out of the wired buildings before detonation. Until a private members' club used by city stockbrokers was bombed in '79 and twenty-three people died in the explosion. I remember that the Brigade's leadership put out a statement expressing their regret at the deaths and the serious injuries that the bombing had caused but their 'military' leaders were rounded up and Coney Island was placed in Army 'lock-down' while the arrests were made. It was called *Operation Zog*, consisting of road blocks and dawn raids, and then the Albanians on Coney Island rioted for a few days in that freezing December. The papers dubbed it the 'Winter of Discontent' but what was left of the Brigade's leadership eventually called a ceasefire by promising to bring an end to the bombings.

Strangely, and contrary to Luke's expectations, the ceasefire actually marked the beginning of some behind the scenes negotiations which eventually led to Coney Island having a small degree of regional autonomy for local laws that didn't contravene the mainland state's imperatives. I guess that could have been good political negotiations on the part of the state in not being seen to be just an oppressive force but one that could accommodate some of the

Albanian people's desire for more control of their life on Coney Island, if not on the mainland itself. Whatever the judgement on this, Luke remained convinced that the Albanian people had a just cause and it's in keeping with his convictions that he went there to support it.

'This one really needs no introduction, Cap, but just in case, it's credited to John Lennon with the Plastic Ono Band. It's on the Apple label and there's no mistaking its message. I first heard it back at the old house blaring out from Luke's bedroom...'

53

In A Broken Dream

'*I remember picking up this glorious single from Ryan's Records, Cap, that slightly dodgy shop at the top of the Victory Circus shopping mall. It was in the autumn of '72. I think it was a cash-in on Rod Stewart's recent success as a solo artist and also with the Faces, as he'd recorded this track originally back in '69 with Python Lee Jackson, a few years ahead of his chart hits. I always think of it now in the context of my relationship with Elaine and how it turned sour shortly after we got married. We went along to some counselling sessions with a woman from the charity, Relate. It was quite daunting to have some unwelcome perspectives unveiled...*'

The sessions took place down south in Burley Way. On Monday nights after work. Monday and Friday nights were usually Committee-free nights for Elaine. She was looking really pale in those days. She'd lost the radiance that I'd remembered from our first meeting when she was at Binfield General and from the time when she lived and worked at the care home in Binford. Had I really taken that from her in such a short time of living under the same roof? From the tenor of those discussions with the Relate counsellor, it seemed that I most definitely had.

'The counsellor must have been about forty, Cap. She had a kind but weary face, frizzy hair and she wore one of those baggy multi-coloured jumpers favoured by the post-hippy fringe of the late eighties. She opened proceedings by congratulating us on our courage in coming along to discuss our relationship difficulties and invited us to articulate our reasons as to why we'd come here today. She looked at me as if to invite me to go first. I turned to Elaine to see if she wanted to proceed instead. She did. And the exchange went something like this...

'Where to begin? It's just that... when we were living apart, we seemed to get on so much better. But since we've been living together and now that we're married, well, I just feel that Lug just takes me for granted. We don't have any quality time together anymore and it's just like we're putting up with each other.'

'Enduring, rather than enjoying?', Rainbow jumper woman ventured.

'Yes. And I even find myself disliking him sometimes. It's so strange. I used to love being around him but now it feels like we've drifted so far apart.'

'Thank you, Elaine. So, Lug... how about you?'

'Yes, I find it strange too. Elaine's right when she says we've drifted apart. She seems to have lost that spark she used to have. And the lack of spark in our relationship has had a negative effect on me too. I feel like I'm to blame somehow. I do tend to go and do my own thing now that we seem to have lost our bond.'

'Thank you, Lug. I'd just like to ask you how old do you feel?'

'I'm sorry, how do you mean?'

'Let me rephrase that. I know that you are twenty-nine but what age do you feel you are now?'

'Gosh. I feel like I'm eighteen still.'

'And Elaine, how about you?'

She looked so drained, Cap. She just said, 'Fifty.'

'Old enough to be Lugwin's mother then?'

'Yes. And it does feel like that sometimes. I feel like an old nag, getting at him to tidy up after himself. It also gets to me that he's not pulling his weight around the flat... and I wonder if he'll always be like this. I've put all my energies into my work lately as it's been difficult to face life at home, with him.'

I remember bowing my head in this public shame, Cap. Obviously, I could have done more to rectify the domestic side of our life without too much difficulty but it felt like the issues were much more than that. Somehow or other, I'd upset her much more deeply. Getting to the root of it was difficult to discern but there was something in there about me no longer captivating her interest anymore as she focused her attention on the council work and its various committees. It's sad that it fizzled out as it did. She'd told me that she loved me about a week after my mum died. Within five years, she couldn't tell me that again. I couldn't take that uncertainty and then I withdrew.

The counsellor concluded by saying that she could help us to separate if we decided that we couldn't save the relationship. Thankfully, we did at least part on good terms. Looking back, I think that I should have tried harder but it did feel too late even at the time.

I hope that she's doing okay at Speedwell. I haven't heard from her in some time now. I think that she was wary of winding Donna up with any contact with me but I did send her a card with a letter at Christmas telling her that I've moved, so I hope to hear from her one of these days.'

52

Mixed Emotions

'I finally got to see the Stones, Cap, back in the summer of 1990. Elaine had moved out to her own flat overlooking Booting Common and I had even more time to 'do my own thing', as I'd said to the Relate woman. Now one of those things was to go to Albania. You could only go there via an organised tour party back then.

I'd first become fascinated by this isolated enclave as a child when listening to Radio Fun in the afternoons and how the siren of Radio Tirana could just be heard encroaching on Fluffy Oldman's show back then. Then, of course, there was the Albanian Civil Rights Movement over on Coney Island, the emergence of the Albanian Brigade and their various 'spectaculars'... and so, I hear you ask, how does seeing the Stones and going to Albania square this particular circle?'

I met Donna at the airport. She'd been keen to join me on this trip ever since I told her about it a few months before. She'd just split up with her latest fella – she seemed to get through them quickly – and we agreed that we'd holiday together 'just as friends', seeing as we were both unattached and that it would be good to have some company, even within a tourist group.

I spotted her from some distance away in that busy terminal. I loved her flamboyant style of clothing. Though she was generally dressed in black, she always had some exciting variant on show. Today's offerings were thigh high leather boots and a floppy hat. Her bright red lipstick even outshone her rubicund cheeks that late morning. And, as far as friendships went, it was definitely one of the more tactile ones. She gave me a big hug and a sloppy kiss on the cheek as I arrived. She was drinking back then, so we headed straight to the bar.

'Well, it was in that limbo period when I'd split up from Elaine and the first time that I'd gone anywhere significant without her in the five years that we'd had together. Though I was hugely excited to be heading out to this mysterious country, it was weird to be doing so without her. I felt a huge sadness one early evening when I was gazing over towards a Communist Party rally in Gjirokaster, the hometown of the former dictator – sorry, Party leader – Enver Hoxha, wondering what Elaine was up to, how she was managing in her new flat, whether she was happier now…'

When I got back to the hotel room, Donna asked me if I was okay. She'd seen me from our window whilst I was down below and she must have discerned that I was preoccupied by something. She was very perceptive when it came to body language and reading people's feelings. I explained that I'd just been 'distracted' by thoughts from home and that Elaine was still playing on my mind. She was good about it. Though we weren't in a relationship as such, it was pretty clear that our friendship was at a new

141

level simply by our going away together. And it also meant that I wasn't thinking about her. Donna liked to be the centre of attention and I've always found it difficult to lie. So, it was a bit of a risk telling her but she listened and she understood. She reassured me and said, 'Well, Lug, I'd be surprised if you weren't thinking about her and what's happened. When you come away from a situation, you can sometimes see it a bit clearer from a distance. Anyway, I've left the bath water in for you if you want a bit of a soak before we go for dinner with the gang. We've got about half an hour.' She was a good organiser too. And I needed that sometimes.

'*... and what life was going to be like when I returned to Booting. Though I'd lived by myself for several years previously, it was quite lonely being at the flat now and my new-found opportunities to 'do my own thing' weren't all joyous self-indulgence. Being away though was a great thing to have arranged in the circumstances. There were some interesting people amongst the tourist party and I found it fascinating travelling around Albania, though we weren't allowed to approach the Albanian people and vice-versa.*

However, one guy defied those rules in what was a hugely brave action. His name was Lorenc. He was waiting near the tourist bus when it stopped in the grounds of Kruje Castle. I was wearing the Stones' tour tee-shirt that depicted a wild cat-like figure and I was also sporting garish shorts when I stepped down off the bus. He greeted me and said it was 'a pleasure to meet a true English gentleman'! I certainly didn't feel that I looked like one and he commented on the tee-shirt, saying that he'd heard the Stones on our state's Worldwide Broadcasting

Service, even though Albanians were forbidden to listen to this decadent western imperialist propaganda. Lorenc said that he'd learned to speak English through listening to the WBS too and he certainly spoke it very well.

Lorenc was a doctor and it was his ambition to come to England one day. But it was still very difficult for Albanians to leave their country at this time, ever since the end of the Second World War. He did make it over eventually and I was able to put him up at the flat in Booting until he was able to obtain a posting to Coney Island Hospital where he could enhance his Albanian medical qualification to the equivalent level of our state's Membership of Physicians.

Meeting Lorenc in Albania was a great part of that trip to Albania, Cap. It made it real and it was a happy outcome from a time of hugely mixed emotions for me. So, from their album 'Steel Wheels', here's the Stones...'

51

Wake Up (Next To You)

That night in Gjirokaster was the first time that I shared a bed with Donna. As distinct from our 'sleeping together.' But it was just sleeping together. And it was very welcome too. Especially feeling the joy of affection and intimacy once again. I think that was what was so sad about the break-up with Elaine. Not only falling out of love but the withdrawal, distrust and estrangement that followed. But the Relate counsellor did help that separation to progress on better terms and that was at least something. I think that at some level the intimate connection was still there too as I did feel guilty about sharing a bed with Donna, even though Elaine and I were now apart. I never told Elaine that I went to Albania with Donna. I think that would have been seen as some kind of betrayal. Or at least a huge lack of decency.

'I still get dreams about Elaine, Cap, about the break-up. They're a bit like when someone you love has died but then they reappear in your dream and you think how are you here when you're dead? And you think for one wonderful moment that they're not dead after all. That you can enjoy this time together

again. But a bit later in the dream, you know you're deluding yourself. I guess Tommo would have suggested that it's all part of the 'grief resolution process' or something like that. Then, of course, I wake up and she's not there. Maybe because I wasn't that good at the grief resolution, I initiated my relationship with Donna far too soon. And then that created its own set of problems eventually. But at least she brought me here... to Harbour Head. I fell in love with the place immediately. It was like a trip back in time almost. It reminded me of aspects of the Binfield that we grew up in. A slower pace of life, people who have a bit more time for each other, a sense of things being more easy-going, and just generally a more relaxed way of life.

This track by Graham Parker and The Shot, from the album 'Steady Nerves', released in 1985, brings this broadcast to a close, Cap. I'll be sending it to you care of Speedwell and I hope that you get it before you leave there.'

THE CAPTAIN'S LOG:
March 12th, 1999

And meanwhile in the hinterlands several miles north-west of Binfield, another musical memoir is about to begin.

50

Betrayal Takes Two

Well, it was certainly a surprise to receive these cassette broadcasts from The Emperor. We're now approaching twenty years since we last saw each other. And my, what a lot has happened during this time. Sadly, I don't have access to much of the music that I'd like to play currently but I do have a Walkman and a few cassettes, and this track from Richard Hell and The Voidoids is on one of them. In fact, Richard and the band provided one of the greatest musical cameos that I've ever experienced back in early 1979 and The Emperor was with me that night at the dear old Hammer' Palais in the far west of the city. They had such energy, dynamism and drive. And so did I back then. It was also a great pleasure to be gig-going with my old friend. Only a few months before it all went sour.

That time was in the very early May of that year. A balmy evening in the Old Town. I crossed the railway bridge at the foot of the steep hill that separated the Old Town from the steep hill up to the Broadway and I headed over to the Smack Inn to see The Emperor. From the bridge, I could see him going into the alley at the far side of the Smack. By the time that I descended from the bridge, he was canoodling with Louise. They were embraced and she was kissing him. I couldn't believe that he would do that to me. Louise had ended our relationship just a couple of weeks before. She was my first 'proper' girlfriend and the first one who I'd lost my heart to. And my virginity. I felt nauseous. I walked away. It was just too much. I kept walking. I ended up down at the brook. I felt some solace down there. I stayed out all night.

Louise breaking up with me had a really bad effect on my mental health. Though, of course we didn't really talk about 'mental health' at that time. I became all too aware of it shortly after though. I was unable to concentrate on anything. I lost my confidence and I felt desolate without her. Looking back, I can see that it stirred up what the people working in mental health term 'unresolved issues' about my parents. I'd been abandoned by them but I didn't know anything about who they were or the circumstances of my abandonment and it was something that my grandad wasn't prepared to discuss until I was older.

My grandad had been in the Binfield police force and there were certain things that he wished to keep secret. That attribute was helpful to me when I was 'laying low' after my disappearance. He was able to use his contacts in the force to stop any further local press or media coverage about that after my return home. He and my grandmother also kept my whereabouts quiet too. I didn't go out and I didn't want anything to do with anyone for quite some time. I've had to come here to Speedwell a few times too. They know me pretty well now. Doctor Beradi suggested that I should keep a journal of events and thoughts that have been part of my day. So that's how 'The Captain's Log' idea started out. I'm breaking it down into musical chapters just like The Emperor has done in his broadcasts. His betrayal was the event that led me into the start of this spiral. And I always think of him and Louise back at the Smack when I hear this track. It's still not an easy listen but it's a significant part of my life and you can't erase your past no matter how much you might like to.

49

Standing In The Road

My grandad Joe Wyndham was a controlling man. I say 'was' but he is still alive. However, he's unable to be quite so controlling since the onset of dementia following a stroke five years ago. He's recently had to go into a sheltered care unit on the seafront called Pier View Court. He's now quite settled there, thankfully. It had been quite a struggle for my grandmother, Ruby, to manage Joe's wandering behaviour in the months leading up to his admission to Pier View Court, or PVC, as we now call it.

What finally convinced the mental health professionals that Joe needed care was when he was out on the busy arterial road one night trying to direct the traffic. Someone called the police and they tried to take him home. They first took him to his childhood home near the seafront as that was the address that he gave them. They ended up taking him to Speedwell where he was assessed on their 'elderly mentally infirm' ward, Glendale. Ruby had been exhausted that night and she slept through the moment when Joe headed out in the early hours. When she woke and reported him as a missing person, the police were able to tell her what had happened.

I've got Elaine to thank for arranging Joe's 'placement' at Pier View Court. She was the manager of Binfield House, the sheltered care unit there, prior to her recent promotion within Dave Paynter's 'Mental Health After Care Sheltered Housing Support Scheme'. She's done well. But she deserves to. She's got a natural way with people with dementia as well as those of us with mental health problems.

So, this 'chapter' in my Log harks back to one of my first ever record purchases back in 1972. It's by Blackfoot Sue and it's on the Jam label. I think it was the first record that I bought that The Emperor didn't already have. We'd seen the band play it on *Top Of The Pops* that summer. I did relish having that record and playing it to him when he came over. It often had to be when my grandad was at work though as he hated pop music. I bought a pair of headphones as soon as I could in order to avoid Joe's ire. Now it reminds me of when Joe went out on the arterial road that night late last year. I find it a tad ironic that he was still trying to be controlling by attempting to direct the traffic – a hangover from his days in the force, of course – although it was this behaviour that brought him to the attention of his successors in the local constabulary and it was their involvement that led eventually to him being in a safer place. I don't think that there's a moral there but it feels like there should be.

48

When I Was A Boy

The Emperor's cassette broadcasts have evoked quite a few memories and he's right when he describes how music can take you back to the past. This track, a B-side, does that for me too. It's by The Who and it's a John Entwistle song. 'The Ox', as John was nick-named, is the lead singer on this one. I think that it sums up how much better my life was at the drawing board stage. Before the frustrations, the betrayals, the onset of mental illness and my revolving door visitations to Speedwell and the various residential homes where I couldn't settle. I don't think that I'm ideally suited to being around people but I have found a bit more inner peace at *The Captain's Cabin* which is in the woods at the foot of the Wrestling Fields, as the Emperor noted via Hippy Johnny's reportage.

I guess that it's all about hope. Back when I was a boy, even though my home situation wasn't ideal, I still had hope that I might achieve something in this crazy world. It all feels so arbitrary though. Whatever hope there was soon diminished as I first became aware of the 'persecutory thoughts', to use Doc Beradi's words, that emerged in my late teens. It was why I was quick to judge The Emperor when I saw him in the alley with Louise. It was an automatically negative interpretation of what I was seeing. Louise, although she was drunk when the canoodling happened, told me that I'd misinterpreted this incident when I came across her many years later. And it's a strange coincidence that The Emperor has also experienced his own dalliances with the altered states of perception that come with this mental ill-health terrain.

I too look back fondly on our carefree days down by the brook and all our childhood fun recording the *Radio Binfield* shows together. The Captain and The Emperor. We were a great team. I'm hugely sad that my suspicions of others have propelled me away from the friendships that I had in the past. Though I am also pleased that some people have never given up on me either. Take Pete Thomas, for example. He's been checking up on *The Captain's Cabin* and bringing me in some music too. And Johnny Green too. He knows one of those traveller guys near me and even they've been looking out for my base. Maybe there is hope. But maybe it's best not to expect too much to come from it.

47

Between Today and Yesterday

I was intrigued to discover that The Emperor would have liked to check out the wooded area in the Wrestling Fields to see if I was living there. Well, it's become a bit of a 'no-go' area for outsiders now that the established group of travellers are in residence. People who do stray into the occupied site of those woods take a bit of a risk. Pete's been seen there a few times visiting me before my latest stay here so it's ok for him now.

I was drawn to the area after learning of my father's death nearby. Pete's mother, Mrs Viv Thomas, who was also an English Literature teacher at Pouk Hill, had been friends with my father before he left Binfield to live over on Coney Island. She told me more about his story than my grandparents have either been able or willing to. Mrs Thomas said that my dad was involved in the Albanian Civil Rights movement and that he became radicalised following the assassination of their mayoral candidate, Ramiz Kreshnik, in 1968. She also believes that shadowy figures enlisted by the authorities were probably responsible for my father's death, an apparent suicide by wrist-slitting back in late '78. I guess that we'll never know for sure.

Shortly after my twenty-first birthday, my grandad had explained to me that Dad was from Albania and that he'd arrived here as little more than a baby on a ship called *The King Zog* in April 1939. *The King Zog* had docked at Coney Island and this was in the days when the Binfield police force also covered the Island too. So, Joe was dispatched there to help with arranging for the refugees to be looked after in the Church halls on the island until they could all be checked out and placed in boarding houses. Joe told me that just as he was finishing his work there, he literally picked up my baby dad from a group of women who had been looking after him. They'd been instructed by the baby's mother, who was too ill to travel following the death of Dad's father during the battle against Mussolini's invading troops, that he be handed over to 'the authorities' on his arrival here. So, Joe took him home to Ruby as Ruby was unable to have a child of their own. It sounds incredible now but they were very different times, of course.

I understand that Dad left Binfield a few months before I was born. I know even less about my mother. She left the area too, I'm told. My grandparents adopted me formally and it's their names on my birth certificate. I know that Joe called my dad 'Louis' but Mrs Thomas told me that Dad reverted back to his Albanian name, Besik Musta, after he went over to Coney Island to try to connect with the Albanian community there. Mrs Thomas said that Dad had kept in touch with her by letter and he said that he would never come back to Binfield whilst my grandad was on the scene. Mrs Thomas used some of those letters to write a book about Dad called *In Dreams Begin Responsibilities*. It's been a good way of getting to know him better.

And talking of writing, I love The Emperor's fusion of music and memoir that he's compiling and assembling via these cassette broadcasts. I haven't played this particular track, which correlates to my own musings here in the Log, in quite a while. It's the title track of Alan Price's album released in '74, and those opening lines about not seeing his mother's face or feeling his father's hand certainly resonate for me. I think that Doc Beradi will like this connection when we have our next discussion about my progress.

46

Captain Fantastic and the Brown Dirt Cowboy

*H*ere is my last Log entry for today. The Emperor's recollection of our Binfield Hall football days reminded me of a very positive session that I had with Doc Beradi last time out. As usual, I was sitting at ninety degrees to him. He always has the chairs arranged that way. He asked me how I thought I was 'progressing' since I had to come back into Speedwell again. I told him that I thought that I was 'doing okay' and that 'the persecutory thoughts and voices had eased off somewhat, thankfully'. Here's how it went, more or less: –

'Good, Winston. That is heartening to hear. And how would you like things to be in future, once you're ready to leave here again?'

I had to think about that before I automatically replied. The sign on his wall opposite me that said, 'Don't just say something, sit there', always made me hesitate instead of saying the first thing that came to mind.

'Now that is a very entrancing question. Bear with me on this, Doctor, but what I would like very much is to be The Captain again.'

I recall when that camera clicked and there was a flash in Binfield Hall's main hall. I felt my eyes flicker in response. I was holding the orange Mitre size 3 football between my legs and I was sitting between my team-mates on the centre of the bench. The photo showed my beaming sense of pride too. I loved those second team shirts with their maroon and white quarters. They were the old first team shirts up until a year earlier. Mr. Newsome had taken me to one side a few days earlier, on the Tuesday after the upturned fingers incident. He was surprisingly sympathetic to my frustrations and he had a plan. And I was at the centre of it.

'Tell me more.'

'Okay. Years ago, back at my old junior school, I experienced bitter disappointment when I was dropped from the school's football first team and I was displaced by a boy called Trevor Moore. I'd vented my upset by gesticulating rudely to the teacher who picked the team, Mr. Newsome, after I scored against Eastchurch. Although I never played for the first team again, the incident led to a happy denouement in that Mr. Newsome made me the captain of the second team.'

'And how did that make you feel?'

That was such a fantastic feeling. No-one had placed their faith in me like that before. And it's only happened ever so fleetingly since.

'It was one of the best feelings that I've ever experienced. Probably only ever surpassed by the birth of the twins. I'm longing to get that sense of responsibility and purpose back in my life. I often feel that I really should have done so much more. But I know that when you have a 'condition' like mine, then it's going to affect your life chances. And I've got to get over that. I want to be leading from the front once again and not just following. I feel like I should be directing things, not simply reacting to whatever circumstances beset me.'

'This is a really encouraging development, Winston. How do you intend to achieve your aim?'

'I believe that it's really a state of mind. Something to integrate into how I look at the world. And how I wish to be. I've faced bitter disappointment again fairly recently. But I'm not going to let that bring me down. I'm going to change things for the better. I've been inspired lately by some communication from an old friend. He once thought of me as The Captain too. And he plugged into my love of the music as a conduit towards this search for meaning. When I get out of here, I'm going to mine that resource. And I believe that this will help me to find something that I can work towards, a new path. I know that sounds somewhat portentous but it's that little bit of hope that might just deliver. Only time will tell, of course.'

Captain Fantastic and the Brown Dirt Cowboy. Well, I've been more in the mire many a time. It's time to shed the brown dirt, even though I still want to live in The Captain's Cabin deep in the woods. I don't have many records by Elton John. But I love this album and its title track. I'm going to play it again when I get out of here as it's going to be the soundtrack for a new era. The Captain is on his way back and he will be a better version of me very soon.

'Of course, Winston, but that does sound fantastic indeed. I've an idea that might help. Perhaps you can bring me one of these tracks that resonate with your search for meaning to our sessions. We can consider them together. I can arrange for the Music Therapy Department to help obtain the tracks you need if you like.'

STEVE MARMITE IN THE AFTERNOON

I loved Steve Marmite's *Afternoon Show* back in the early-mid-1980s when I was doing the morning or night shifts. Steve and his 'Afternoon Gang' were highly amusing, with a whole host of zany guest characters. I especially liked 'Damien, the social worker' and his elongated use of the word 'community'. Steve and his gang were a joyous source of community support for me back then, especially when I had some difficult times. And I'm glad that Steve is still going strong on *Radio Snooze* these days too.

45

Is She Really Going Out With Him?

'*Welcome back, Cap. We're now in a different era of the old Radio Fun shows, moving into the eighties with Steve Marmite. I was working shifts during the early eighties and I often heard Steve's shows, which were generally quite entertaining what with his quirky array of characters. Not everyone enjoyed Steve Marmite like I did though and you either loved his show or hated it.*'

Spring is definitely in the air here on Harbour Head. We've had the first wave of holiday-makers down for Easter and plenty more have been sticking around since. It's a delight seeing people enjoying these light evenings around the harbour too. And Oscar is revelling in the attention he gets whilst perched on the gunwale of the *The Southern Star*.

'*Though this track did emerge twice in the late seventies, initially in late '78 without success but re-issued in the Summer of '79, when it became a Top Twenty hit here in Blighty, it's the kind of track that would most definitely have been played on Steve Marmite's show…*'

And just over on the other side of the harbour, beneath

those Regency-era buildings positioned precariously before a cliff face, I see her for the first time since the new year. She's not alone though.

'… and it came to mind again after seeing Donna walking hand-in-hand earlier this evening with… wait for it… Bonk Tripego! I know, Cap, I couldn't believe it myself either. How does he do it? Well, I know that he's exceedingly tall, dark, slim and to some eyes, handsome, but it still amazes me that he's able to inveigle his way into places that he really should be denied access. I think it's his downright shamelessness that gets me. I know that it's dodgy territory to be thinking of an ex in a paradigm of possession but I always felt that there was an unspoken code where you didn't pursue a friend's former partner. Not with this guy though. Twenty years on from his shenanigans with Louise Robinson, he's now up to his old tricks with Donna. Yep, there's something going wrong around here, Cap, and Joe Jackson is gonna tell it like it is…'

44

Young Hearts Run Free

Being aboard *The Southern Star* and looking out on Donna and Ben in their relaxed togetherness on that sunny evening somehow took me back to 1976 again. I think it was something about being aboard a big boat or small ship and my memories of the *Bembridge* disco ship back in the Old Town. It was Ben who loved hanging out there in particular. I think it was the Louise Robinson association too. And before Ben started pursuing her and before even The Captain was with her, Louise and I had a thing going on.

'*Seeing Bonk with Donna brought all those Louise issues back again, Cap. I know that it was twenty years ago now but it's still clear in my memory. I think that what was different about our love triangle is that it was conducted without rancour and deceit. When Louise and I split up, it was on good terms. We wanted to be 'just friends' and you and her got on so naturally that, well, it really didn't feel like a threat to my world. Sure, there were times that you two wanted to be alone together but we were still were able to meet up for gigs, go vinyl hunting at the record shops and hike out to those jam nights at that Zero Six club way out on the fringes of Beastwood. Our friendship really wasn't affected by our respective relationships with Louise... at least not until that night that we don't mention...'*

And it was Ben who encouraged me to ask Louise for a dance. The good thing about those discos on the *Bembridge* was that there was a diverse array of music. It wasn't all the classic disco sound. However, as far as disco-type records went that year, this one by Candi Staton provided a joyful juxtaposition of great vocals with an upbeat feel but bittersweet lyrics too. I'm a big believer in the self-preservation that Candi sings of, rather than consigning myself to a relationship that's not going to work out. Well, until Donna came along, I guess. I think that I stuck at that one for so long due to the failure I felt about my marriage to Elaine disintegrating. That, and because I'd moved a long way down here to Harbour Head to be with her.

'... and I never harked back to my time with Louise, though it was only for a short while and several months before you and I became friends again in 1977. Now this particular selection might surprise you but I adored it even though it wasn't really hip for us blokes to like disco pop back in '76.

I remember you walking around the school back then with albums by heavy metal bands under your arm and this record was as far away from that as you could possibly get, but it still stirs me to this day. There are times, Cap, when I think that I'm living the messages of this record, if you can excuse the gender disparity, and how I really am not suited to relationships. But credit where it's due. Louise loved this record. They used to play it at the Bembridge in that glorious summer of '76 and she'd go off with her mates and dance so freely to it. It was really nice to see.

I've been wondering, Cap, if those days are gone forever? It would appear so. Just like the tennis courts of our youth, I think that I belong in that lost world of Binfield from yesteryear. I wish I could go back just to taste it all again. I often wonder how Louise is now too. I'm feeling that I'd like to do a George Bowling trip as he did in 'Coming Up For Air' and go back to Binfield to see if I can rediscover that spirit of our youth. But we both know how poor old George's re-visit turned out...'

43

Oh No Not My Baby

'*This is from the period when Rod Stewart's solo records were still very good, Cap. This one came to mind earlier this evening when Donna paid me a visit...*'

I was enjoying the April afternoon sunshine out on the 'weather deck' when she came into view, rounding the grass promontory of the road at the harbour's head. She walked languidly, which was uncharacteristic. She was alone, thankfully. She waved to me when she got closer.

'I thought 'this should be interesting' as she approached The Southern Star. I helped her aboard. She looked pale and less confident than usual. She wanted to go inside so that we could 'have a talk'...'

'Lug. This isn't easy...'

She's going to come clean about Bonk.

'...but you of all people have a right to know...'

Yep. Confession time.

'... that I'm pregnant.'

What?

'And I'm going to have the baby.'

Is it mine or his? It was just over three months ago that we

167

were together in the cabin.

'Good. And congratulations. How far are you?'

I took in a deep breath through my nose.

'Six weeks.'

It's his. Slow breath out.

'Well, I'm really pleased for you. It's what you've wanted for some time.'

This really hurts but platitudes must.

'No, not like this. Ideally, it would have been planned. Ideally, it would have been...'

'*...yours.*' *Mine. My baby too.*

She broke off and looked away.

'*... and then she talked about how Bonk had turned up at Homely in February. How it was really cold and 'blowing a hooley' outside. How she couldn't leave him out there on the veranda. How they bonded over hot drinks by the fireside. How he offered to help her with those house jobs that needed doing. How it was nice to have male company again. And so on and so forth...*'

So, she decided that now she was pregnant by Ben that they were going to be together.

'*...and that Bonk was now living at Homely. He'd split with his wife shortly before coming down here to check me out, but Donna had at least put him off my track, as I'd asked...*'

And, as always seems to happen, we decided that we would remain friends. I wished her well and told her that I hoped 'everything goes well' as I helped her down the gangplank before she set off back around the harbour towards *Homely*.

'*And there you have it, Cap. It's quite taken me by surprise.*

And I think that I must have been suppressing all that child wish stuff because, just for a moment, I was hoping that I had a part in the creation of Donna's baby. But it wasn't to be and now I'd like to entreat you to this fine version of this Gerry Goffin and Carole King penned song. It reached number six in the UK charts in the Autumn of '73...'

42

My Ever Changing Moods

'*I used to love it when Steve Marmite would introduce a record by The Style Council, Cap, with just the laconic and pleasingly disrespectful remark of 'Here's grim-face,' a reference of course to their singer and creative spark, Paul Weller. Well, this fine track, which I have here in the vinyl twelve-inch single format, has been an enduring weathervane for what's been happening in my life for fifteen years now. I remember that you once said that the best records can take you through the good times as well as the bad times and this is certainly one of those…*'

Donna's news sent me into one of my depressive turns. The Producer was 'up country' at the time doing his bit to sell the community radio bid to the *Jackpot* panel for their prospective funding. One of the new volunteer guys, Terry, was helping me with the technical side of my show whilst Ray was away. I found it a bit difficult to concentrate at times and Terry could see that something was wrong. I was able to confide in him what was playing on my mind and he sat in with me during the shows to help me through them, keeping me alert to cueing up the tracks correctly, ensuring that I had the right faders up or down, and he also had the salient information handy about the tracks that I was playing. You know the kind of stuff : how this record was released in February, 1984, and got to number five in the UK singles chart.

'And it hits my current mood too. I've been feeling a bit down since Donna brought me up to date with the big events in her life. I'm surprised by the effect that it's had on me. We'd not only split up several months ago now but I'd also decided not to pursue our more recent reconvergence too. It was clearly over. I'd voted with my feet by not traipsing back to Homely. I may need to rest a bit before committing some more tracks and thoughts to this broadcast, Cap, 'til this cloud passes over. In the meantime, here's grim-face...'

41

Destiny Calling

It didn't take long before that downbeat mood hit the up elevator. In the shape of the Producer hurtling up the gangplank on that sunny spring day. He had some rather good news.

'Welcome back, Cap. It's been a few days since I last broadcast to you but I had to come back 'on air' to tell you of a wonderful development here on The Southern Star. The Producer's only gone and hit the jackpot with Jackpot! Our community station has got the state casino funding and will soon have its own FM banding spot on the dial. You should have seen the Producer's face as he came bounding up the gangplank. I've never seen him so animated! It was a strange delight. His natural countenance at rest is a tad lugubrious but today he was grinning almost continuously from the moment he came aboard…'

Ray burst into the cabin and grabbed me by the shoulders, as his rubicund face gleamed even redder than usual.

'Luggy, my boy – we've done it! We're going to go national next month! The *Jackpot* panel loved our idea of music-related storytelling for radio and they've backed us with the big bucks to get our station on the road. Well, obviously, more on the sea in our case, but you get the idea. They loved the samples from your shows and how you were able to bring your pithy short stories to great effect around your choice of record. I can't thank you enough for your pioneering work for the station. Hold on, I think I can and here's how…'

'… and he was so chuffed that his plans had paid off after the tortuous application for the Jackpot funding. He was complimentary about my humble contribution to his presentation, just some recordings of 'Our Tunes' type montage of music memoirs that I do in my show and about how well they'd gone down well at the funding panel's deliberations. Anyway, he wanted me to go off and have a holiday before the station's waveband launch next month and he stuffed my shirt pocket full of 'mauve-backs' to ensure that I'd take off and get a good rest. I told him about the Donna stuff too and he thought that it was essential that I get away and clear my head. He's going to look after my dear little Oscar for me and I'll contemplate where I'm heading next.

Before I do though, let me just play this modern record from last year and we sure don't get many of them on my broadcasts. This is by a band called James. And it's going out with huge thanks to the Producer. He's got big plans and they're now on the bus that's sign-posting 'Destiny'!'

THE ROAD SHOW,
with assorted jocks

Come in 'Smiley Miley', come in... we need to hear how far you've travelled to get from yesterday's venue for the Road Show to today's one. How I used to love the dear old *Road Show*. It was the sound of summer on *Radio Fun*. Those daily weekday outdoors summer holiday shows used to take place around the country with big audiences in various locations. It had an air of 'fun' about it which was largely due to the enthusiasm of the jocks concerned and their mostly teenage audience. And I wonder if Smiley's still out on the road these days too...'

40

Journey

'*G reetings, Cap! Apologies for being away so long but this has been a bigger trip than I'd expected. This section is a homage to the Radio Fun Road Show which used to take place in the summer. You'll no doubt remember that it had a revolving array of the Fun jocks, including Dave E. Playlist, Peter Smile and Paul Brunette, as well as the ones who we've already featured on these broadcasts so far. I came away on my journey 'up country' with a Dictaphone so I could record some thoughts whilst on my travels and now, with thanks to the Producer, I'm reunited with my tape-to-tape recorder and a whole lot of cassettes so I can put together the commentary and the music once again. This one, by Duncan Browne, was released in '72...'*

The Producer gave me a lift to Line's End station which is about twelve miles west of Harbour Head. It's the most westerly railway terminus on the mainland and it's a small but charming reminder of the early Victorian style ensuing from the 'railway boom' of the 1840s. It should ideally be viewed via a monochrome prism but even in full technicolour, it still has a glorious retro feel about it. It's over five hours 'up the line' to the city and it takes in some fine coastal scenery in the early stages of the journey. And I think it was sometime about halfway through the journey that things took a strange turn.

'...and whilst I was on the train heading towards the city, I had a feeling of disconnectedness and a strange, light-headed sensation. I don't quite know what happened after that but I'm told that I wandered into a record shop in Edmund Hill, in the north-east of the city, and that I was talking to myself as I perused all the records, commentating on when they were released and seemingly having conversations with an imaginary someone about music.'

39

Purple Haze

'I've had a few vague flashbacks to that record shop, Cap. I understand that it was called 'Purple Haze' and I can vaguely remember going through one of the racks there whilst I was hearing voices. They were the voices of the DJ's who I remember from Radio Fun. They were talking to me about the records that I was looking at. I also heard your radio voice as The Captain and my own one as The Emperor. I don't know how long I was there for. I can also recall wandering through a shopping mall and coming down an escalator into the high street. I was told subsequently that the proprietor of the record shop was concerned about me and that he'd called the emergency services as I didn't seem to be aware of what I was doing. He was also disconcerted because, at times, I was speaking quite loudly back to the voices.

There's only one record to play here, of course, and it's by Jimi Hendrix...'

38

Everybody's Talkin'

'**M**y memory is a bit clearer for what happened next, Cap. My head was somewhat scrambled by the different voices talking at me and I just had to lie down on a bench in the high street. Some people came up to me. They tried to talk to me but I couldn't hear a word they were saying. Apparently, I'd tried to give some of them the Producer's mauve-backs. Eventually, the paramedic guys arrived in their groovy green uniforms and they helped me up into the back of the ambulance. And that's how I ended up at the North City Hospital for a few weeks.

This is a song written by Fred Neil but I'm going to play you Harry Nilsson's version...'

37

Can't Get It Out Of My Head

When I was well enough, a kind and highly astute doctor explained what he thought had happened to me. I think that this was a few days after I'd been admitted.

'The exact details for the times of various events after my 'psychic retreat' is all a bit blurred, Cap. Once my psychotic symptoms had stabilised after taking medication for a few days, Doctor Beradi – or 'Beardo' as I named him, but not to his face – sat me down and explained my 'condition', based on what I'd been able to tell him, and also from the reports of the paramedics who'd brought me in and the nursing staff who'd been observing me over the previous few days...'

My first impression was that Doctor Beradi was not much older than me. I'd say that he was in his early forties. He was slight and slim in build and he had a nice line of corduroy trousers in various colours depending on the day of the week. I'd observed brown, racing green, grey, black and dark blue. He didn't work at week-ends.

'So, Beardo believed that I'd experienced a dissociative state of 'fugue' on the train journey up here, a reaction to trauma. I recalled that I'd been fretting about the Donna and Bonk

179

scenario once again on that early part of the train journey that I could still remember, so that may have been the trigger. Or maybe also coming back up here too. It's the first time that I'd been away from Harbour Head in quite a while.

And the business in the record shop with the voices was indicative of an acute psychotic episode, but me trying to give away money to the concerned people who were checking on me and me talking about being 'The Emperor' also led Beardo to think that there was an element of hypomania in there too. With my past history of depression thrown in as well, he came to the conclusion that I was suffering from a 'schizo-affective disorder', but he preferred to call it a 'psychic retreat' as this described a safer space psychologically for me to withdraw to, following the upset of Donna being pregnant by Bonk.

It all makes a kind of sense, Cap. I guess it just goes to show that I'm still somewhat emotionally brittle these days after previously thinking that I'd got on top of the depressive aspect of my character.

This one's by the Electric Light Orchestra and I remember that they used to play it on Radio Mariline back in the mid-seventies. It's got a wistful, dreamy feel about it. A bit like how my head feels now that I'm on the anti-psychotics...

36

Alice

'**B**eardo explained that as the psychotic episode had come on quickly and acutely, then my prognosis for a full recovery was very good. He stressed that I needed to take the medication to ensure that would be the case. He also made time to see me each week to check out my progress and help me to explore some of those upsets from the past as he believed that they could still be unsettling my 'equilibrium', even now. He was particularly intrigued by this dream that I had about you some time ago which had recently returned to my thoughts.

I was at an Alice Cooper concert, quite near the front, and during one of the songs that he played from the 'Welcome To My Nightmare' album, Alice says your name, looks towards the back of the auditorium and tells you that you've got to go home now...'

I felt very at ease with Doc Beradi. When I'd done my psychiatric nurse training some fifteen years or so earlier, the Consultants always came across as somewhat aloof. Doc Beradi was much more down to earth and approachable. He had a very calm manner and he always listened carefully to what was said to him. I felt that I could confide

181

in him in that short time that I was at the North City Hospital.

'... *and I explained the background to the dream's denouement, where I'm following you out of the concert hall and you hit the street just as I come through the foyer trying to catch up with you and then I shouted after you 'Hey, Wiz – it's not what you think! It's not what you think!' and how that was what I imagined I'd have shouted to you had I seen your departure after the alleyway incident...'*

Doc Beradi was also interested in the musical associations in my dreams and I told him about how this musical memoir came about from my time at SPiBU, a few years ago. He thought that was a useful way for me to discern connections to some of those underlying scenarios that might still be troubling me. He also arranged for me to join a music therapy group which was run by the unit's occupational therapist.

I found that the other participants had various problems ranging from anorexia, depression, hysterical conversion and obsessive-compulsive disorder, but we were the gang who were still in better shape than most of the in-patients, and it provided a relative sanctuary from some of the more disturbed moments that you might see or hear from back behind the locked door.

Just in case you've not witnessed scenes like these, I'm referring to the times when a patient might be experiencing an 'episode of distress' and an assembly of male nurses, some from other wards nearby, gather round and one of them tries to persuade the patient to take some medication. If he or she refuses, they're bundled into a side room and thrown face down onto the bed where a hypodermic containing the 'chemical cosh' – it used to be haloperidol back in my day – is plunged into the upper outer quadrant of one of their buttocks.

'... *and talking of Alice, here's a brilliant track from Mott The Hoople's great album from 1974, 'The Hoople'. I don't have the album with me currently, Cap, but it has one of my favourite covers. You remember it? A lovely vibrant blue background with the head of a woman with an afro and the band members' faces hidden in her curls.*'

35

On The Road Again

I managed to get out of the unit relatively quickly on the understanding that I was going to be staying with my doctor friend, Lorenc, over on Coney Island.

In my last meeting with Doc Beradi before I was shown the unlocked door to the acute unit, he arranged for me to check in with him two weeks later for an out-patients' appointment at Speedwell, the nearest psychiatric hospital to Coney Island, where he also had a gig as a consultant psychiatrist.

And the Producer was happy for me to extend my 'up country' sojourn for a bit longer as my DJ stand-in, Katie, was doing a great job on the new station, *Starboard FM*. So, I could get this show on the road again, armed with a fistful of chlorpromazine pills to keep the voices at bay. And some procyclidine poppers too, to counteract the possible side-effect of limb stiffness.

'Hey, Cap, this Dictaphone is coming into its own now. I'm speaking to you almost live from the top deck of the number 251 bus. You remember the green Eastern National bus which goes all the way from the north-east of the city to Binfield-on-

Sea, taking in all sorts of out of the way, Hicksville places in the countryside? I've already seen some of those football pitches that I used to play on in the Binstead District League with Haydn the social worker, so it's been a bit of a wander down memory lane. Hey, this place looks familiar too… it's North Bindown, which is not that far from Speedwell, actually. I think that this was where me and my brothers had that car accident.

Ah, it's come back to me what we were doing over here that Saturday. We'd been to see my auntie Jeanie in Speedwell. She was the first person I'd seen who had a mental illness. Or a 'mental breakdown' as they called it back then. Her husband, my uncle Barry, had been killed in a motorbike accident a few months before. I liked uncle Barry. He took me out in the little side-car attached to his bike when I was a kid and it was really exciting. The Health and Safety commissars of nowadays would certainly not have been impressed with that! It was still in pre-safety helmet times when Barry was cut up by a car swerving in front of him and Barry came off the bike when it skidded after he had to brake sharply. So sad.

Poor auntie Jeanie was very pale and she looked so gaunt. She was still unable to speak and she just stared into the distance. We didn't stay long. When she was better, she said that she had been aware of us there, but she felt that her voice was trapped. She said that she didn't have the energy to speak. She had to have ECT. Electro-convulsive therapy. I think she was at Speedwell for several months before she came out. She was never really the same after. She always had an air of sadness hanging over her. She seemed to convey a deep and dispiriting world-weariness. It didn't occur to me until now just how

185

much history of melancholia we have in our family, as I also recall my dad having a lugubrious aspect too…'

When I got to Binfield bus station, I rang Lorenc and told him that there'd been a change of plan but that I was hoping to see him in a few days. He was keen to check out that I was okay. I reassured him I was fine and I explained that I just wanted to spend a bit of time back in Binfield before coming out to see him. Then I checked in to a guest house near Binfield Central station.

'… particularly after the arguments with Mum. I ended up staying in a guest house near Binfield Central with her once after this massive row they had where she ended up chucking a table chair through the front window. I think that I was about four years old as I can't recall going to school from the guest house on the next day. Hmmm, talking of guest houses, I think that I'll check out the situation when the dear old 251 comes to the end of this journey. And when I'm re-united with my records, I'll be putting this one by Canned Heat on this broadcast for you. It'll be seamless. That's the joy of almost live broadcasting here on Radio Binfield…'

THE CAPTAIN'S LOG,
May 14th, 1999

Meanwhile, back in Speedwell...

34

Comeback

The release date beckons. Doc Beradi's talking about next Tuesday, after his ward round, if everything carries on 'progressing well'. He said that he'll start me off with a period of leave from the ward for nearly a week first and then he'll have me back in here for the Monday night ahead of the ward round on the following day, just to make sure that I'm good to go. He's been impressed by the development of what he calls my 'engagement with Radio Therapy'.

Since I told Doc Beradi about the fusion of the music and the memoir that The Emperor has inspired me with and its reminder of our personal radio station, *Radio Binfield*, from our childhood days, he arranged for me to have sessions with the ward's occupational therapist, Justin, who is a bit of a tech-head with all this modern MP3 digital music world. They've got some impressive equipment down in the music therapy department, as well as old school turntables and cassette recorders too. Justin's shown me how I can download the tracks that I need for my compilations and how to 'burn' them onto a CD. And from there, I can record the track onto a cassette broadcast, just like Lugwin's been doing.

'Welcome back to the solid gold sound of Radio Binfield! This is your Captain calling and I'm going to start off this show with one of my favourite artists. Here's Glen Travis Campbell with a record that speaks so clearly to me. I hope that you like it. I know I do...'

33

Lorraine, Part 2

Doc Beradi was intrigued by my reflections upon my family history, or at least the parts that I know about, and how I was able to link them to music which resonated with my own talking interludes. Thinking about my history in the recent years with this place, where I've almost acquired a second home and family during times of difficulty, I've been thinking about the previous occasions that I prepared to leave. And one occasion in particular from nearly ten years ago now.

'This one by Legend, from their 'Red Boot' album of 1970, reminds me of a Lorraine who I used to know. I was in the same class as her at school back then, though I didn't know of this track until many years later. Probably only a short while before she wandered back into my life once again…'

I was told that I was going to have a visitor. Someone called Lorraine Paynter from a 'community care' organisation. And lo and behold, she was a grown-up Lorraine Robinson. At one time, I think nearly all the boys in our class back at Binfield Hall had a crush on her in the year or two before we left for our respective 'big' schools. She was still hugely attractive. And even more self-assured. She wasn't surprised to see me because with a name like Winston Wyndham, it was unlikely to be anyone else. She'd come to see if I might be willing to consider staying in a 'residential placement' on leaving Speedwell. She suggested that it might help with my 'rehabilitation' after being here for a few months following another 'episode of paranoid ideation', as Doctor Waller, the doctor who I had at the time, described it.

Lorraine wanted me to talk about the various things that had led to me being in and out of Speedwell. So, I recounted the story right from the start: – the difficulties with the discipline of my grandad when growing up, the feelings of alienation at Pouk Hill, the upset with Louise, the belief that Lug had betrayed me, the mystery of my real parents, the feeling that I'd wasted my life since the onset of the mental illness, the repeated flare-ups of my 'condition' when I felt that I was being persecuted by someone or a group of people. At that particular time, I'd thought it was the travellers living nearby. It certainly felt like a well-rehearsed series of lines from a play that I'd been starring in.

Lorraine listened intently and she let me finish before interjecting any comment of acknowledgement. She didn't make any judgements either, which was reassuring. She seemed to understand the feelings that I had expressed – the hurt, the frustration, the occasional bitterness towards others. It was her kindness of response that led me to take up the offer of a 'temporary placement' at the residential unit. Though it didn't work out, as I'm not suited to these group living situations with their repercussive social dynamics, particularly with the types who seem to thrive on a bit of fake drama, I was glad to have had some time in her company again and that temporary placement was a helpful 'bridge' to returning back to my cabin in the woods. Most of my traveller neighbours seemed pleased to have me back there and I was really chuffed that they'd kept an eye on the cabin for me too.

'... and this one's going out to Lorraine for being a person who I've admired as both a schoolfriend all those years ago, and for being kind and sensitive in her professional role as a concerned adult in these more recent years. I'm sure that whatever's she's doing now, she's doing it really well, and still in a compassionate way too.'

32

Funny How Love Is

This place has certainly given me a fair share of introductory meetings. Including one with the mother of my children.

I first met Elaine when she was working on Plashet ward in late '93. I was in again for one of my 'revolving door' stays. Elaine was a student nurse back then and she asked me if she could interview me for a 'case study' for a 'module' that she had to complete for her psychiatric nursing course. I was delighted to. I hadn't been delighted about much for years but she certainly lit up something inside of me from the moment that I first met her. I think it was the genuine interest and positive spirit that she conveyed. And a hint of vulnerability too. There are some hard cases who work in psychiatric hospitals. Though Elaine could be resolute when she needed to be, it wasn't the armour-plating that was to the fore in her case. It was her humanity.

After meeting Elaine on the ward and telling her about my history, she arranged to do a 'community follow-up' of how I was managing back in the real world when I got out of Speedwell early in the new year. My cabin was not the ideal place to host this, primarily because it was stuck out in the wilds and because it could be intimidating for any strangers to wander into that wooded enclave where they'd be likely to be treated with suspicion by its inhabitants.

We met up at the White Hall, near to the southern tip of Binfield Valley Drive. Just along from the tennis courts where Viv Thomas used to play in mixed doubles matches with my father before he went over to Coney Island. The White Hall used to be the club house for the tennis players but now it has various groups and societies running there. Every Wednesday, there was a drop-in centre for people who'd recently come out of Speedwell and also for anyone who needed advice on benefits.

I think that it must have been someone who worked there who 'shopped' Elaine to the Nurse Education Centre at Speedwell when it became apparent that our meetings were looking more intimate than just my 'community follow-up.' It was extremely harsh that they dropped her from the course. But the head nursing tutor decided that Elaine had transgressed the boundaries of the 'nurse-patient relationship' and so she had to leave Speedwell and the nurses' home there. She lived with me in the cabin for a short while before she got a job with Dave Paynter's care team at Binfield House, a residential unit for 'mentally infirm' older people at Pier View Court, a former hotel overlooking Binfield Pier. There was also accommodation for staff at good rates and it was a lot more comfortable for her there than it was at my cabin.

We used to meet up in town after her shifts and we'd go

to gigs at the Railway Hotel, a music pub near Binfield Central station. It was a joy to have trust and affection back in my life again. I was able to stay with Elaine in her room at Pier View Court back then. I respected her need for space too after her busy work schedules, so we only met up once or twice a week and sometimes more when she had the week-ends off. It was probably the most 'well' that I'd been in years. It all changed after she became pregnant, sadly.

Elaine began to resent me for these major changes in her life. She'd enjoyed the psychiatric nursing and she'd not planned to have children. Learning that she was pregnant with twins was a massive shock to her. She was able to stay on at Pier View Court, or 'PVC' as we called it, whilst she was on maternity leave.

Dave Paynter was good to her. Just before she had the twins, he arranged for her to live in the manager's flat at PVC as his wife Lorraine didn't need it anymore. I think that was a shrewd move on his part. Elaine became the manager there shortly after she returned to work as Lorraine had started a new job in the city.

Elaine made it clear that I wasn't welcome at PVC anymore and it was her mother who stepped in to look after the twins whilst she was at work. Dave Paynter had also arranged a creche at PVC for the staff with children and I know that helped Elaine's childcare arrangements too.

Funnily enough, I still see Elaine here on the ward from time to time. She's taken over the management of the new 'Sheltered Housing After Care Support Scheme' now running at Pier View Court and she interviews prospective residents from amongst the patients for 'placements' at PVC if they're unable to go back to their previous home. She keeps it professional with just a brief acknowledgement of me when she passes through the ward but it's always a reminder of the distance between us now after what was the most joyous time that I've had in years.

'A truly bittersweet one this, from the Fine Young Cannibals. It's a track from their eponymous debut album, released in 1985. I'm certainly not the only one to have loved and lost but that doesn't really make it any easier...'

31

All The Way

'*New Order have been there for me throughout all my 'mental illness years'. This one though really hits home with its lyrics about finding the truth inside yourself and not depending on anyone...*'

So, my parents abandoned me. My grandparents withheld the truth from me and there are still parts of it that I don't know. As for relationships, well, in the most significant ones, with Louise and Elaine, they both rejected me. And I also thought that my best friend betrayed me. I can see that differently now but it was too late to prevent the spiral that ensued from that night in the Old Town.

Even before his recent broadcasts from *Radio Binfield*, I still thought of The Emperor from time to time. And in contemplating this track and its meaning in my life, I'm always taken back to the winter of 1978 and a poem that he wrote. He wouldn't have written it ordinarily but we had to write a poem of our own for the Mentor's class. Lugwin called his one *Control* and the last line said it all really, '*The only way to go is your own.*' And that's something that I've felt a need to do during all these years of uncertainty. I had hoped that it might be different with Elaine. But it wasn't to be. She decided that she would rather bring Louis and Lorraine up without me.

But I'm actually not that resentful now. With all these situations, it's not just about me. I guess everyone involved had their reasons along the way. I know with Elaine that she felt that she couldn't rely on me in the longer-term. It wasn't just the uncertainty of how my 'condition' might represent. She was also concerned that I wouldn't have the 'staying power' to commit myself to the parenting of the twins and she wanted a consistency of care for them from the outset rather than any uncertainty about what I would be able to commit to, particularly as she was determined to try to juggle parenting with her work too. She also didn't want the twins getting too used to me being around when she felt there was a big chance that I wouldn't be there for them in the future. I tried to reassure Elaine that I was committed to their parenthood, but she had made up her mind about this even before she gave birth to them.

'I admire people who can act in such an independent-minded manner. I guess at some stage, we do need the help of others though. For me, over nearly two decades, I've needed the sanctum of being here at Speedwell from time to time after it's all got too much to handle beyond these doors, walls and gates.

But I do like the idea of being able to stand apart from previous things that I've said or done. We all change and I wouldn't like singular aspects of my history to define me, even if they did seem significant at the time. Otherwise, there'd be no hope of 'moving on', as per the repeated mantra of this millennium age.

Maybe the key to maintaining hope for the future is to work out what can inspire you to keep going and try to derive some joy in our daily activity. The music has always been there for me. And writing about it as part of Doc Beradi's 'Radio Therapy' has been providing me with some of that impetus too. It's definitely something that I want to continue.

In the meantime, how about I play the record? It's time for less talk and more music, to coin a phrase that I'll probably repeat intermittently here on Radio Binfield...'

ROUND TABLE,
with various jocks

This show used to take place in the *Radio Fun* schedules on late Friday afternoon until the early evening. It was fantastic to hear the new releases with various DJs in the chair back in the late seventies and early eighties. I loved hearing the opinions of their weekly guest musicians too.

30

My Little Town

'*I'm sure that you'll remember that this Round Table show on Radio Fun used to take place on Friday afternoons, Cap. I'd get to hear most of it after returning home from school before heading off to the pub or even a gig.*

Kid Handsome was the first jock who I definitively remember hosting it in the late seventies, although I have a vague memory of the original Emperor Boss Co. doing so a few years before. I'm sure you'll recall that the DJ hosting it would also have a special guest to discuss the new releases with.

I don't know if this one from late '75 was reviewed on the Round Table back then but I'd be surprised if it wasn't, as it was Simon and Garfunkel's first release together in the five years since they'd split. It was on my mind once again when I started my tour around Binfield and its immediate environs...'

I meandered around town and then I marched out to its north-eastern corner for a good mile or so out to Binchurch cemetery, where I could pay my respects. It had been quite a while since I'd been out there.

Their grave had subsided a bit in that time. The heart-shaped headstone that I remember Mum discussing with a sombre-suited man back at the old house in the aftermath of Dad's death still looked quite imposing. Those lines inscribed on it that she approved, *I could die by your side in the discontent that I feel*, certainly reminded me of her upset on those Sunday afternoons that she took me there after *The Big Match* was on television. That was back in the days before video-recorders and she always allowed me to see the football highlights programme before we headed off to the cemetery.

Mum's ashes are just behind Dad's headstone and it seemed right that they're together there. Mum's headstone is much smaller. It's in the shape of an open book and it sits a short distance in front of Dad's. It describes her as *A loving mother and grand-mother*. I planted a kiss from my lips to my right index finger and the middle finger and then onto both of their headstones before heading back towards town via Binchurch Park. I never could linger at the cemetery for long.

'Binfield town centre's always been a busy place, Cap, but it certainly seems busier these days. Sad to see that Guy Norris Records is no longer there in Victory Circus though. You probably know that its once sacred space has now been usurped by a carpet store. Carpet-baggers indeed! No Kelley's Records either down the High Street. I used to love playing prospective singles in the booth they had downstairs there. But there's still The Golden Disc, thankfully, though it does look a bit ramshackle these days.'

29

Down By The Seaside

'*I know that you were always more of a Led Zep fan than me, Cap, but I love most of their album, 'Physical Graffiti', including this track. I was reminded of it when I walked through town and then stood gazing out at the majesty of our dear old Binfield pier.*

It was quite clear out to sea, or across the estuary, and I could see over to the mainland on the other side, several miles south of this still magnificent and lengthy platform. I saw families walking together on it and I was reminded of those Saturday mornings in the summer back in the mid-sixties when I used to hold Dad's hand as I peered through the gaps in the boardwalk at the incipient tide below whilst we ambled to the end of the pier, stopping occasionally to look at the big fish swimming near to the pier's pillars. Dad was clued up on the various types of fish around there and he told me that they were grey mullet.

When we finally reached the end of the pier, Dad would buy me an ice cream with a flaky chocolate finger in – it was called a '99' for some reason – and then we'd get on board that little train which bumped its way back to the pier's terminus. I

*loved those rare moments of intimacy that I had with Dad and
they remain a treasured memory now…'*

The childhood reminiscences came flooding back on a
walk along the prom heading west towards the Old Town.
I passed the stretch of beach near Bincliff jetty, where Mum
used to take me during those mid-sixties' summers. I
remember Mum being so much more relaxed down there
when she sunbathed on her lounger. That was when I'd go
out onto the estuary mud to see if I could scoop up some
crabs with my sand-bucket. It was near to the candy floss
kiosk where my brother Jack used to work in the summer
holidays.

Some later memories returned too, including lying on
the spacious green above Bincliff beach in that glorious
summer of '76 with Louise Robinson whilst my radio cassette player belted out our favourite songs. And, of course,
the *Bembridge* – it's still there, pleasingly. The thrilling
flashback to that night when Ben Trippier alerted me to
Louise looking my way all those years ago. Those flashbacks were quite powerful and though they were mostly
happy ones, I felt a great sense of loss too.

Thinking back to that late afternoon going into early
evening, and in particular the memories of me and Dad on
the pier, I think that the feelings of loss now revolved
around a realisation that I was unlikely to become a father
myself. Though it was still biologically possible, as I was
thirty-eight years of age, I felt that I didn't have the emotional stamina anymore to try to hook up with anyone
towards that end. I also didn't want to be one of those
beleaguered older dads who struggle to keep up with the

vitality of youth. And, of course, there were my own mental health issues now. If I had difficulty looking out for me, how was I going to be able to look out for someone more vulnerable?

'It was a bittersweet walk down by the seaside, Cap. I was assailed by images from so long ago and it dawned on me that grief is quite tidal in its movement. At low tide, you can be paddling away and almost have forgotten your loss momentarily... but then, seemingly from nowhere, when the high tide sweeps up on you, you can suddenly feel overcome by its force again...'

28

I'll Show You

The gentle surf was brushing up against the rocks below as I strolled along the footpath next to the railway track towards the Old Town. It was a regular service bringing back Binfield's commuters from their work in the city. I was hoping to find one of them at the Smack, the first pub you come to when you hit the Old Town from its shoreline's eastern approach. I wasn't disappointed.

Scotchy was sitting outside, just opposite the pub at a table under the railway bridge. He saw me first and called me over.

'Good heavens, Lug. Fancy seeing you back here. Sit yourself down and I'll get you a drink. What's it to be?'

This one, Cap, is by Dexy's Midnight Runners. It tells the tale of seeing old school friends now grown up and how they've turned out. Funnily enough, I actually saw Dexy's with Scott and Pete Thomas back in early '81 up in the city.

I saw 'Scotch' outside the Smack on the day that you got discharged from Speedwell. He told me that Pete was planning to take you back home and help you get in any things you needed on your way back.

Scotchy also did a running commentary on the people coming in and out of the pub and reminded me who they were from our younger days. As you can imagine, he was pretty scathing about everyone who we saw that evening, except for one person. And I was quite taken aback to see her there...'

27

Louise

'*She still had that nifty afro that I remember from '79, Cap. She looked well, albeit a little careworn. I saw her go into the pub and Scotchy, seeing my attention drift from his latest diatribe about one of the pub's other habitues, told me that Louise was working there some evenings. 'And damned good she is too', he opined.*'

Scotchy called Louise over when she was outside collecting glasses and he smiled as he asked her, 'Now then, Louise, I don't suppose that you remember this old chap?'

Louise's green eyes narrowed as she scrutinised me. She drew a breath and said, 'My, oh my. It's Lug, isn't it? Didn't you move away?'

'Yes, Louise. It's really good to see you. I moved away twenty years ago. I live way out west now, down in Kernow. Just popped back for a bit of a holiday. How are you doing?'

Louise frowned slightly as she picked up our old glasses. 'Ah, so-so. Tell you what, I'll be able to have a bit more time to chat when I have my break just before nine. Really lovely to see you, Lug. Catch up in a bit.' She gave me such an enchanting smile. As if we were still lovers.

'*I don't know if you remember this one from 1984, Cap. I recall that DJ, Mike Lead, who was at the helm of the Round Table then, and when he interviewed his guest Phil Oakey, the lead singer and creative force of the Human League. He asked Phil what plans that he and the band had for the forthcoming year. Phil's reply was fantastic: — 'To do as little as possible for as long as possible.' How great is that? Anyway, I know that you'll love it, especially because of its talky bits and Phil's reflections on how it's not always true that time heals all wounds. And then that killer line... 'there are some wounds that you don't wanna heal'. Wonderful stuff, Cap. I hope that it's as evocative for me as it is for you...'*

26

Old Friend

'**I** enjoyed catching up with Scotchy that evening, Cap. He seems more at ease these days. I told him about my misadventure on the way here and the background upset with Donna's pregnancy and Bonk's re-emergence. He mused on how having a child was 'of course, something that would never happen for me' and we talked about how a weight has lifted from him in being open about his sexuality now. I told him that I'd always thought he was possibly more asexual than homosexual and he said I'd probably formed that impression due to him still being 'in the closet' back then…'

'And now?'

'And now, I'm still just a straight-acting queen. 'Coming out', in that horrific phrase, hasn't actually changed how I am. But it changes things for some people. Particularly people who I've heard make homophobic remarks before. Not to me or about me but about other people. They've either kept their distance since or they've gone out of their way to tell me that they didn't mean to be offensive. The way things are, it's like there's always got to be some form of scapegoating going on. Now I remember that you used to be a fan of Tom Robinson. We're going back a few years now, of course. I thought that he was brave with that *Glad To Be Gay* track from way back when. But I couldn't admit to it then.'

'Ah, yes – early '78, from the *Rising Free* EP. Certainly a contrast to the band's 'everyman' hit, *2-4-6-8 Motorway*, in late '77. Seeing 'TRB' live shortly after *Rising Free* was released was a huge moment for me. I thought that they were a great band then. And Tom made a big impression on me with his politics. Some of his more recent stuff has been pretty good too. I need to do you a compilation tape when I get back to Harbour Head.'

'This one, Cap, is from Tom Robinson's 1984 album, 'Hope and Glory'. I did see him at that time at 'the Stiffs', as we used to call the Cliffs Pavilion, with my brother Luke in late September that year. The magic had gone somewhat but I'll always have a soft spot for Tom. I've been enjoying some of his releases from earlier this decade though. And I discovered this one on a great compilation album. I find this track quite moving and I love the line about how the protagonist can start to 'see' his old friend and now know him as he really is.'

25

Like A Rolling Stone

Scotchy wasn't able to stay out in the Old Town for too long. He was due to meet up with our old friend Prov at a pub called The Cliff, not far from Bincliff station, just west of Binfield Central, and he was just having 'a few looseners' before getting on the train. I was amazed at his stamina. He's always been a formidable drinker but he seems to be in a whole new stratosphere now. We agreed that I'd send him the cassette broadcasts that I'd been recording for Wiz to pass onto his brother Pete, as Pete was the only person who we knew that had any contact with Wiz.

I headed inside the Smack towards the bar where Louise was serving. It was quite busy and she needed to work really quickly there by herself as the other bar staff were all taking out food orders. It was a far cry from the old days of my youthful drinking. The only food that you could get there then was a pickled egg, some peanuts or crisps. Also, there had been a public bar and a saloon bar. Now it was all one distinction-free bar. The doorway in a partition wall leading out to the back balcony overlooking the estuary was no longer there. Nor was the juke box that had been near to that partition wall, which was itself no longer there. I thought back to that glorious old juke box and when it used to blare out Bob Dylan's *Like A Rolling Stone* on those Friday and Saturday nights of my adolescence. The record seemed to go on forever. Though it was thought of as an 'ancient' record in my late teenage years, it was still hugely popular with someone or some people at the Smack back in those days.

'Hey, Cap... going into the Smack and seeing that the lovely old juke box was no longer there reminded me of the times waiting at the bar when 'Like A Rolling Stone' played on, seemingly interminably. Then that got me thinking about seeing Bob Dylan at Blackbushe in '78. He reworked a lot of his old songs and he had a reggae style going on for some of them. It felt like a huge occasion and I was there more out of a sense of curiosity rather than as a fully paid-up fan. Funnily enough, apropos of the previous selection, I was wearing a Tom Robinson sweat-shirt to denote my contemporaneous allegiance from back then.

And I also remember that you always felt that 'The Zim' had a habit of giving us 'one verse too many', but this one has really grown on me over the years. I picked up the original vinyl single in the market that Donna had a retro-clothing stall in. It's got a few little crackles at the start but the sound has so much depth compared to the CD version I also have. In fact, I'm going to ensure that you hear that crackly single version when I get this talky bit linked up to the records again...'

24

Peaceful Easy Feeling

'**H**ey dreamer, what are you drinking?'

Louise's words jolted me out of my reverie. I hadn't noticed that all the other punters who were at the bar had been served and now it was my turn. I'd also just noticed that Louise, despite her careworn countenance that I'd observed outside, had a renewed confidence and an apparent 'at ease'-ness with me. It helped me feel at ease too.

'I had a good catch up with Louise, Cap. I didn't have any idea that she was married to Bonk. Well, not any longer. They divorced earlier this year. She's been working at the Smack for the last few months in addition to her day job as an English teacher at Pouk Hill in order to keep up with the increased mortgage payments since she bought him out. No wonder she looked tired.

She told me that she'd seen you a little while ago and that she put you right about what happened in the alleyway that night. I'm glad that she told you. I don't know if you've got that early broadcast that I sent you when you were at Speedwell, the one where I tried to explain what happened. But it's good to know that Louise has explained it too. Though she did seem out of her head on that night that I helped her out of the alley, so I'm doubtful that she would have been able to remember that much. Anyway, I hope that might have helped to ease your discord towards me and that maybe one day we can be friends again. I'd like that very much. In fact, I don't think that I'd be whole again if not. I've got a good feeling that maybe one day it will work out okay. I certainly hope so, my dear old friend.

I've come to the end of this one now, so I'll get this off to Scotch and hope that Pete can get it to you soon. In the meantime, get your old cowboy boots on and shake 'em along to the sound of The Eagles, in dedication to Louise, the woman we both loved... and lost. I'll be in touch again when I've completed the next broadcast. Keep that FM247 frequency open and don't touch that dial!'

THE CAPTAIN'S LOG,
May 21st, 1999

Meanwhile, deep in a wooded area at the southern end of
the Wrestling Fields...

23

On The Air

*T*he old place was in pretty good nick seeing as I'd been away for nearly three months. I really appreciated Pete's visits here in keeping the cabin warm and clean in my absence. I appreciate it also that he doesn't crowd me and that we don't feel a need to meet up too much. I value my space nowadays very much and the lack of social obligations that I have. Some people crave company. I'm not one of them. Losing Elaine and the children was a part of that. It hit me hard and I retreated into myself once again.

I'm feeling more positive than I have done for a while though and I'm sure that the radio therapy has been instrumental in this. Doc Beradi also arranged for Justin, the occupational therapist who helped me with the MP3s, to pop in and see how I was doing yesterday. He didn't stay too long so I think that I must have passed the safety test, the one where they check up on you to see that you're safe.

I told Justin that I'm going to continue with the radio-style broadcasts which have helped me to express some of the thoughts that I've had. I think that I'll try to connect with Elaine in this way now that I'm in a better state of mind and see if this might help to open up the channels of communication once again.

'Well, hello. Welcome to my newly rediscovered medium of communication. I've been trying this out whilst I was in Speedwell thanks to a discussion with Doctor Beradi about ways of helping me to express my thoughts. Doing this helps so that some thoughts don't get to play on my mind and turn ugly.

The Doc has described this as 'radio therapy' as it's a fusion of music and talking about it. I find these personal radio broadcasts to be a good way of connecting with whatever's going on for me but they can also be a good way of sharing some of these thoughts too with a selected listener 'out there'.

And today, you've been on my mind and I was hoping that you might hear me out. I'm going to start off with this track which I know you'll know as you were a fan of Peter Gabriel ever since his time with Genesis. This one is the opener for his second solo album. It didn't have a title as such, but it's known as his 'scratch' album due to its cover photo depicting him scratching downwards from what appears to be the inside of the camera lens…'

22

Island Hopping

The personal radio broadcast provides me with a wonderful blank canvas upon which I can etch my varied thoughts. When you're engaged in a focused effort though, in connecting to 'that one listener out there,' you've really got to go personal. Start off with a wide-angle lens and then hone in. But with Elaine and where I'd like to be with her, I've got to go steady.

'It's an absolute joy to be back here at the cabin. I'm indebted to Johnny Green for building me this little lean-to out the back where I can sit shielded from the rain by this cast-off Perspex-panelled roof. I love the sound of the rain on it. Also, the sound of my seagull visitor pitter-patting across the roof before it dips its beak into the guttering to forage for some water.

I cherish this sanctuary. I'm even at ease with the now-rooted travelling gang holed up nearby. They've made it clear that they don't want to infringe upon my space and they've also provided security for the cabin whilst I've been away. Our contact is not of an intrusive sort, thankfully, and I now feel that I could go to them for help if ever I needed it. Maybe that's a sign that I'm getting better with groups of people now. And maybe Joe Strummer was right when he said, 'Without people, you're nothing.'

You know more than most how I've shied away from any crowds and limited my social contact to the barest minimum that I could get away with. But it feels different for me these days. Somehow, I've had a little faith in humanity restored and I'm not quite so averse to checking out a scene or two. As you know, I moved here to be near to where my father was. Maybe I need to get closer still and check out whether there are still any remnants of his life over on Coney Island. Yes, I'm going to do that. One day real soon.

This one's from 'Earthquake Weather'. It was Joe's first solo album after The Clash folded a few years earlier. I bet Coney Island wasn't in his mind when he wrote this song but it's certainly in mine and I'm keen to hop over there one of these days.'

21

Always On My Mind

'**H**ere's the title track of this broadcast. It's a Willie Nelson song. I'd like to dedicate it to you as my way of saying sorry for not being able to be the person that you would have liked me to be. I regret profoundly not being able to be that person. I'm not expecting any change in the current situation but I am hoping that we might be on friendlier terms one day. I wish that I'd been a better person for you and that things could have been different but I'm a realist and not a dreamer.

And now, like my old friend The Emperor is wont to say, 'less talk, more music…'

THE NEW BLONDE WHISTLE TEST,
with Annie Nightowl

It was hugely refreshing when the first female DJ on *Radio Fun*, Annie Nightowl, started to host the *Whistle Test* music show on television in the late seventies. I also enjoyed her weekly Sunday show on *Radio Fun* too. Annie was far more welcoming of the 'new wave' of music back in those days than dear old Bob Whisper, the beardie bloke they used to have hosting the Test before Annie livened it up. And I love the way that Annie's championed such diverse music in recent years too.

20

Late In The Evening

'*I always enjoyed Annie Nightowl's shows on Radio Fun back in the late seventies and early eighties, Cap. She was quite a champion of the new wave genre of music when I first started listening to her in early 1978. However, it was her stint on the Whistle Test which I remember particularly well from those days, especially when she interviewed Paul Simon.*

It was in late 1980. Paul had a new solo album out. That was 'One Trick Pony'. Dear old Annie, bless her, she asked Paul about his solo career and what it was like writing all the songs now, 'without Art Garfunkel.' Paul was surprised but matter-of-factly advised Annie that he wrote all the Simon and Garfunkel songs. Annie then dug herself in deeper by asking something like, 'Is that commonly known that you wrote the songs?' and Paul, slightly embarrassed, replied, 'Um, maybe by everyone except you, Annie.' I was delighted that the editors had left that all in but I did feel a bit sorry for Annie in that hilariously mistaken moment. This track from 'One Trick Pony', and also a single released in 1980, always reminds me of dear Annie.'

It also reminds me now of that late evening with Louise

when we left the Smack together. She managed to get out of the pub shortly after last orders so that she could get the bus home from Binfield West station in good time. We walked together by the railway tracks and past the cockle-sheds towards the station. It was a quiet and warm night. I had a strange feeling that we weren't alone, that there was someone nearby who was watching us but who was keeping out of sight. Louise took my arm and I felt a thrilling tingle surge through my body.

'I always wondered what happened to you, Lug. I remember seeing you about in the Old Town until you went up to the city just after that summer when Wiz went missing. And that was that. No sightings until today. Though Ben did tell me that he'd seen you up there a few years ago.'

'Ah – I did come back from time to time, Lou. Mainly to see my mum. I just didn't really want to return to the scene here. I felt a bit out of touch with it all. I tended to stay in Beastwood when I popped back. Except for maybe the odd gig at the Stiffs that coincided with those visits. I could be anonymous there, with just me and the music. Looking back, I think that Wiz going missing had a bad effect on me. It was like another death in the family.'

'Yes, I can understand that. And I was sorry to hear about your mum too. She was a kind woman. She always made me welcome when I came over to your place. And it was nice of her to let us go off to 'listen to some records' up in your room.'

A funny thing happened late that evening, Cap, when I was back in the Old Town. I was walking by the cockle sheds with Louise after she finished work and we were heading for the bus stop. I felt that you might somehow be nearby and that you were watching us. I guess that was probably something to do with what happened way back when and my possible guilt feelings about that incident.'

19

(I'm Always Touched By) Your Presence, Dear

Though I smiled at Louise's memory of my mum's relaxed attitude to our record-listening cover story for our convivial teenage times together, she discerned that I was distracted.

'And so, where are you now – my dreaming man?'

'Ha – you always know, don't you Lou? Well, my head is slightly up in those stars tonight. It's truly weird, you know. Being back here with you reminds me of Wiz. And tonight, I feel like he's here with us. I know… it is strange. But I just can't shake that feeling off.'

'I'm playing this one by Blondie, Cap, by way of a reflection upon your apparent presence during that cockle-shed walk. I also heard your voice speaking to me too. And it certainly alarmed Louise when I spoke back to you.'

18

Marquee Moon

I'd stopped on the footpath just before the granite steps up to the station approach when I heard Wiz's voice. Louise had already started to climb the steps when she turned back to see where I was. She'd been surprised by my preoccupation with Wiz and I think that's when she might have known that something was wrong.

'I thought that you were berating me for being with Louise again, Cap. Saying things like 'So how can you be up to your old tricks again, Lugwin?' and 'Wasn't it enough with what you did last time?' and a lot worse besides. I said, 'Look, if you're there, just come out and make yourself known. I can't be doing with the commentary.'

I saw Louise looking back down at me and when she asked if I was alright, it took my attention momentarily away from what I thought was your voice.'

I tried to explain that I'd been on medication for 'the voices' but that I'd left it at the guest house and that I hadn't taken it today as I should have done. Louise said I needed to get back there and take it. And that there was a late train back to Binfield Central which I was still in good time for. But I had other ideas.

'I skirted around the front of the station and went looking for you on the path to the Wrestling Fields. There was a vivid moon that night and I thought that I'd be able to see you if you were around there. Louise called to me to come back. Something in her voice, the concern, alerted me to the possible danger of going any further. I turned back. The bus arrived just as I returned to the concourse in front of the station.

Louise said that I should come on the bus with her. I was still bothered by your voice saying *'this is The Captain calling from FM247 Radio Binfield'* but I tried to focus on what Louise was saying. She told me that I could stay at her place for the night if I wanted.

The lights in the bus were very bright but I could still see the moon's rays reflecting off the estuary's waters through the bus's windows as the bus ascended the steep hill up towards the Broadway.

'I'll play you the full album title-track version of this one, Cap. And what an album it was. I thought Television were a great band for the short time that they were with us…'

17

Shout Above The Noise

I didn't complete that bus journey to Louise's place. Most of it was spent hearing The Captain's voice giving me a hard time about being with Louise. He was accusing me of 'treachery and deceit' and he said that I had betrayed him once again.

'It was very unsettling, Cap. Your voice was so clear – and castigating too. You were saying 'why have you come back here to upset me with this hurtful reminder of what you did back in '79?' and 'Have you no shame, Lugwin? Just go away and leave me be. I'll never forgive you for your deceit and your treacherous betrayal. You were supposed to be my best friend and look what you did. And now, you're going back to her place too! This is all too much. Just go. Get out of Binfield, Lugwin, go!'

I think that I was shouting 'Stop' in response to your niggling at me when the bus driver opened the doors and he shouted out that 'This is your stop' and despite Louise's pleading, he was adamant that I get off the bus.'

I saw Louise waving at me as the bus wheezed off in the direction of Beastwood. I'd been deposited just around the corner from the dual carriageway that led back towards Binfield Valley Drive. The Captain was laughing at me now. I was beginning to hate him. And to hate myself too.

'I think that I was shouting as I got off too, Cap. Back at you, you understand. I realise now that it wasn't you, that it was just the turmoil in my head.

This one by Penetration says it all, really. I'm listening to it in the cans now. I don't have to deal with the accusation that I heard in your voice that night any longer, thankfully. I hope that in real life, though, that you have been able to forgive me for the misunderstandings that took place back in 1979, the year that this one was released.'

THE CAPTAIN'S LOG,
May 28th, 1999

16

Congratulations

'I caught up with Johnny Green at Pier View Court earlier today when I was visiting my grandad. He told me that there are some big changes afoot. And I believe that some overdue congratulations are in order... and that's a 'very well done' on your promotion! Johnny said that you were moving on from your management role at PVC to being Dave Paynter's 'right hand woman' as the After Care service has really taken off in the last few months and that Dave needs your help with the day-to-day running of the show.

Johnny's looking forward to taking over the flat at PVC now you've gone, seeing as he's going to be managing the new unit for the people coming out of Speedwell. He's really excited about that. He told me that he'd pass on my tape to you when I've finished it, just in case you don't get around to telling me where you and the twins will be living now.

Anyway, this is one that even my grandad liked back when I was a kid. It's about the only record that I could think of to fit this moment here on my little broadcast.

And I'm pleased to hear that Joe's been enjoying the music therapy at PVC. He definitely seems a lot more at ease now.

His memory's getting worse though. He called me 'Louis' when he first saw me. It took a little while to get through to him that I was his grand-son rather than his adopted son. And also, he was under the impression that his parents were still alive too. What a horror show dementia is.

Anyway, well done on all your great work at PVC. And thank you for being able to help Joe get there when you did. I hope this gets to you ok. Here's Sir Cliff Richard on the rather pleasing old Columbia label…'

15

I Don't Believe In Miracles

Hey Johnny,

Great to see you this afternoon. Here's that cassette I mentioned. Thanks for being able to pass it onto Elaine and here's hoping that she'll see fit to let me know where she's moved to soon. It's a bit like that Russ Ballard song that he wrote for Colin Blunstone back in '72, about an ex having the grace to let the singer know where they are now. But here's hoping - and I also fully understand that you're not at liberty to disclose this information to me.

To be fair, you've probably shared more than you had to. I appreciate your honesty. And many thanks for all your kindness with my grandad. I'd be delighted to help with your project for the 'Social Care' course. I think Joe's story is one that will be ideal for your dementia module. I'll probably compile it with reference to some music and send it to you via a cassette as that's 'my way' nowadays.

Oh, by the way, talking of moves, I saw your mate Shane tonight and he said that he and his gang will be leaving here soon. They've got notice from the council of a 'Removal Order' giving them four weeks to depart the wood. Luckily, I've not received one but that might be because my grandad helped me move here officially way back in the early eighties. He might have been able to pull a few strings with the council back then as he wasn't that long retired.

I'm sad they've got to go now. Originally, I was really annoyed that they'd moved near my little spot. The whole reason for my moving here had been due to the social misanthropy that I'd developed by that time. It almost charts my progress that I've been able to be more accepting of them and have even welcomed their presence in more recent times. I know that I've had to return to Speedwell in between but, as you know, certain upsets contributed to those episodes.

Anyway, I hope to have Joe's story with you soon.

All the best,

Wiz

THE LATE SHOW,
with John Zeal

I loved John Zeal's late-night weekday show especially for his boyish enthusiasm in his championing of bands or solo performers who were not yet generally commercially successful. I also loved his droll delivery too. I've got out of the habit of listening to him these days, sadly, but he was a great presence on the radio for me back in the late seventies and early eighties.

14

'Seven Minutes To Midnight'

Getting turfed off the bus and having to split from Louise like that left me feeling abandoned. It must have been close to the midnight hour as I trudged by the dual carriageway past Binfield Park, then by the fire station, then past Pouk Hill grammar school. It was eerily quiet along there. There was only the intermittent passing car with no-one else out on the street until I saw an old guy over on the grassy middle area of the carriageway walking a big dog, a Rottweiler. The dog stopped and crouched. The man, tall but stooped, looked over the road towards me as I passed. He looked away when I looked back. He waited for the dog to complete its delivery on the grass and then they dawdled off in the direction that I had come from.

'I think you'll like this one, Cap. I was reminded of it when contemplating the events that happened that summer night on leaving the Old Town and getting dumped off the bus near the dual carriageway that leads to the south-western end of Binfield Valley Drive. I remember that John Zeal championed Wah! And at this time, I think that they were called 'Wah! Heat'. They played it on one of his 'Zeal Sessions' in 1980. I

was an avid listener of his Late Show in those days. I remember that you loved him too. He's been branching out a bit these days what with his homespun tales on Radio Jaw. I've heard some of them and he sounds like he's enjoying that conversational format. Much as I am with you, of course.

So, I was heading towards BVD, and it was the voice of John Zeal talking to me now. I had a moment of clarity and realised then that I was becoming increasingly deranged. John was telling me about Wah! and how he had enjoyed meeting their lead singer Pete Wylie at a gig fairly recently. I felt increasingly jangled through hearing the different voices speaking in my head. First you, then John. And then John suggested to me that I should go have a look at the old house.'

13

Back To The Old House

There are so many memories attached to *Anchorage*, the old house that my dad and his gang of guys built back in the early years of the sixties. When I approached it, I saw that it's a doctors' surgery now. How Dad could have done with a doctor in the house back in late November, '68. That was the night that he keeled over in the toilet. I think that I broke his fall. It's hard to remember all the details. I guess that was a result of the trauma.

The plastic flamingos that used to stand on the borders of the fishponds are no longer there and the ponds have been filled in and covered with shale stones. There's a light on in my old bedroom. On the night that Dad died, I recall laying in my bed when Mum came in. I didn't know that Dad had already died by then. Mum said that he'd been taken to hospital. She asked me if I wanted to sleep in their bed that night. I declined. I feel bad about that now as I guess she must have been pretty traumatised herself. I was only just eight years old though. It didn't seem to be the right thing to be sleeping in your mum's bed anymore.

'I wonder what you would have made of The Smiths, Cap? They were one of the few bands that I cared for back in the mid-eighties. This track, from 'Hatful Of Hollow', released in late '84, is a particularly haunting one. I did actually go back to the old house that night. I stood at the gate and just took it all in, albeit briefly. A great sadness came over me thinking back to the night my dad died there. When I get out of here, I'll pay a visit once again in the clear light of day. You probably know that it's a doctors' surgery now. Maybe I'll get myself registered there if I stick around for a bit.'

12

Police Car

I remember traipsing over the dual carriageway via the grassy tree-lined area in the partition between the roads. Thinking of when me, Wiz and Johnny Reggae used to chuck sticks up at the tree branches to knock down conkers in the late September of 1971. That was one of our forms of entertainment back then and it would last until a bemused motorist would park up, come onto the partition and tell us off when one of the sticks had landed in the road, just a bit too close to the oncoming traffic.

I headed off down Binfield Valley Gardens and gazed up at the little window above the door of the Robinsons' old house. That was where Lorraine's bedroom was. She used to blow the three of us kisses from there in the summer of '71, on the nights when it was getting too late for her and Louise to come out to play. It was just a short walk from there to the brook, past the tennis courts, down near the junction with Southbound Grove. I kept to the road route down to the bridge as it was better lit. Then I popped behind the bridge wall for a pee.

'I went down to the brook bridge, Cap, to have a discreet

241

slash. I was just zipping up and heading back onto the foot-path when two cops approached. One of them asked me what I was doing, where I'd been, what's my name and where I lived. When I told him about 'The Southern Star', being 'The Emperor' and 'FM247 Radio Binfield going national,' he looked at his colleague, then looked back at me and said, 'Well, you'd best come with us.'

I'll sign off this broadcast, Cap, with this one by Larry Wallis, a glorious early Stiff Records release from 1977. I was hoping the cops would just take me back to the guest house but it didn't quite work out that way.'

THE CAPTAIN'S LOG,
June 4th, 1999

11

I'm Weird

Pete Thomas dropped by today and he was surprised to see the travellers' site left abandoned. He's been busy with his new band lately and he appears to be trying to look like Marc Bolan. His hair is all in corkscrew curls now. I asked him about it and he said he can't tell me anything 'on that score yet'. It sounds intriguing. He also brought me a cassette from The Emperor that Scott asked him to pass on. Lug had written a letter that came with it.

My dear Captain,

I hope that this latest broadcast finds you well. This will be the last one that I'll be sending to you. I hope that you've found them of interest and it would be great if they might be effective in helping to restore our friendship, if possible.

I'm currently staying at Speedwell. You'll hear more details in the broadcast but in short, in coming back to re-visit Binfield, I've had a major psychotic unravelling and it looks like I'll be here for a while yet. The Producer brought me up my Dictaphone and my tape-to-tape recorder along with a box of my compilation cassettes. It's been good to get all the developments down on tape and, as they say here, it's been 'therapeutic'.

I'm feeling much better, thankfully. Though I am zonked out for a lot of the time with the medication. I don't quite know what I'm going to do when I'm able to get out of here. It's a bit like that Marc Bolan song 'I'm Weird', from the 'You Scare Me To Death' album, posthumously released in '81. I feel like I'm the weirdest dude in the asylum these days and I'm just going with what the 'multi-disciplinary team' of doctors, nurses and occupational therapists tell me. I've been in a bad way but luckily, I got taken here before the voices could have directed me into more harmful situations. They've subsided now thanks to the olanzapine and the 'MDT' are pleased with my progress.

The Producer also brought me a letter from Elaine. It was quite a shock to hear about all that's happened, particularly between you two. So, now I know that we've got even more shared history than I previously thought.

Anyway, I'm here on Plashet ward if you'd like to visit. Best ring and see if I'm still here beforehand if you do.

All the best,

Lug

RADIO THERAPY,
with Lugwin Loggins

It was Doctor Beradi, or 'Beardo', who described and pre-scribed the treatment of 'radio therapy' for me. He believed that it would be helpful to build on my strengths of using the music to interpret my inner dialogue. He encouraged me to bring some music to the weekly psycho-therapy sessions that I had with him following the initial treatment of my acute psychotic episode. I took along my cassette player so I could play him some music that I'd related to my ruminations.

10

Guts

The Producer hadn't been able to see me until a few weeks after I'd been admitted. He'd been told by the nurses that it wasn't a good idea for him to visit until my condition had 'stabilised' following the early period of my admission. He brought me a letter. I recognised the writing as soon as I saw it on the envelope. I waited for Ray to leave before I read it. It left me feeling like I'd been pounded in the stomach.

Elaine apologised for leaving it so long in replying to the Christmas card that I'd sent last year to her former address at Speedwell. There'd been a delay in her receiving it until sometime into the new year, as she'd moved from Speedwell nurses' home a long while before. She said 'things had become hectic' what with her work, especially more recently with her promotion in Spart's 'After Care' service. And then she told me about how she'd become a mother to twins. And that their father was Wiz.

'Excuse some of the language on this one, Doc, but it's the visceral feel of expression here that resonates. It's by John Cale, and it was released in 1975. It's from his album entitled 'Slow

Dazzle'. I didn't know it at the time but in recent years, I've been going through John's back catalogue. See what you think and I'll tell you the background...'

'It's strange. I don't feel that I have any right to be angry. People 'move on', as they say. But I was angry when I read that letter. And I was in shock too. You know, I'd harboured some misplaced idea that I might be able to get back with Elaine. It was difficult to take it all in. And shortly afterwards, I came 'round to the idea that if two people who you love get together, then that's a good thing. But then they broke up too. So, everything is broken now.'

'Everything, Lugwin?'

Beardo asks short questions which make you sit and think a bit more about what you've just said. 'Don't just say something, sit there.' That's a line from a poster that he had up on a wall in his office at Speedwell.

'Well, maybe not everything. My dream of getting back together is though.'

We spoke about that dream and what Elaine and Wiz meant to me. I realised that I needed them even more now that I felt so alone. But some of these feelings of regret laced with misplaced hopes can just churn up your guts. Some things you have to 'let go', to use another one of those phrases that crop up whenever you can't realise what you'd hoped for.

9

I'll Take You There

And Beardo was right in his suggestion via a question. Not everything was broken. Far from it. We considered other people in my life. Take Ray, the Producer. He'd been there for me when it mattered. Ray Hope. I love it when people's names say so much about them. Ray was such a positive guy. And nothing ever seemed to worry him. I aspired to be like Ray.

Ray had kept me up to date with what was happening back in Harbour Head. Katie, Terry and the band of volunteers who made up the roster of *Starboard FM* had all been doing really well since the station hit the airwaves last month, and Ray was very pleased with how it was going. He told me that my cat Oscar had been loving all the company he had on board *The Southern Star*. I sure was missing the little fella too. But the idea of being a jock on board the boat again felt quite daunting at the moment. Ray told me that the cabin was there for me to return to whenever I wanted and he didn't want to add to any pressure that I might already be placing myself under. So, we kept it as an open-ended possibility and we agreed that I'd ring him on his mobile from the patients' phone every week to update him on how I was doing and then he'd ring me straight back for a proper chat. He also said that if I did decide to come back to Harbour Head when I left here, he'd come pick me up and take me there.

'I've been reflecting on how we left it last week, Doc. I make you right that not everything is broken. This one makes me think of my good friend who got me into this DJ lark late last year after I'd been turfed out of my old girlfriend's place down in Harbour Head. It's by The Staple Singers and it was released in 1972, probably one of my favourite years for music…'

8

If I Can Dream

Since my divorce, my next of kin has been my brother Jack. He was the person the medics or the nursing staff would contact if there was anything happening about my treatment at Speedwell. Doc Beradi asked him to come to his ward round in the early days of my stay on Plashet ward just so I had some family representation to agree my treatment. When I was still hearing the voices, I was deemed to be unable to give informed consent to my treatment. So, they placed me under a 'Treatment Order' which took care of any opposition that I might have to refuse the olanzapine, but it also placed a duty on them to consult with my nearest relative too.

Jack appeared very uncomfortable when he came onto the ward. I tried to find a quiet spot over in the small dining room which wasn't used outside of mealtimes that much. We could chat relatively privately there although we might have one of the roaming, more manic patients coming in and out of there on occasions.

I hadn't seen much of Jack in recent years since I moved from the city out west to Harbour Head. It was good to catch up. He still lived upstate in Spiresville, the university town where he was the head of his college's Economics department. He'd become a father twice in the last fifteen years, to two girls, and he was busy at home and at work. His wife Gina was a teacher so it was action stations for both of them, but they managed. And they loved those long holidays too, always heading off somewhere exotic in the summer.

Doc Beradi was curious about one of my dreams, the one where I'm playing tennis and where I see a figure dressed in black looking on from a window overlooking the court. Where it ends up with me gasping for breath when I can't get the lob that's gone over my head. Then I see a woman beyond the nylon fence who looks away when I fall to my knees. He wants Jack to attend our next session so we can explore it together.

'Well, Doc, it had to be an Elvis record if we're talking about my brother Jack. Jack loved The King. He had all his singles and most of his albums too. And you wanted me to talk about one of my funny dreams too. So, I chose this record. I'd love it if I could be reunited with both my brothers one day but that looks like another forlorn hope at the moment. Still, I can dream and this one always provides me with renewed vigour and inspiration. I hope you like it. I know I do.'

7

Dreamworld's Taking Over

Doc Beradi put me under hypnosis for the dream session and he recorded it. Jack was present too. I listened to the recording afterwards.

'I'm at The White Hall tennis courts. It must be early afternoon. The sun is high and I'm squinting as I wait for the boy at the other end of the court to serve. That boy is Wiz. As he used to be when we were ten or eleven years old. We always used to play tennis in those golden summers of the early seventies down there near the brook. Behind him in the distance, I see a man dressed in black staring at me from the window of the house overlooking the court. And behind me, there's a woman peering through the nylon meshed fence. I turn around briefly before Wiz serves just to see who she is. It's Elaine. But she's so much older now. She looks away when I turn towards her.

And here it comes. A bit of swerve away from me heading to the side of the court. I dart over to the right and just get the ball back but it's only to mid-court. Got to dash back across to try to head it off. He's on it quickly and I see him compose himself just before he lofts it deep over my head and I've got to

254

get back before the second bounce. I'm not going to make it. I'm breathless, my chest is tight. I can't breathe.

I fall and I just see Elaine's dejected eyes turn away once again. She's fifty years old now. The same age as my dad when he died. I'm slipping in and out of consciousness whilst the man in black is standing over me. He has a pale face and a sickly grin. He's counting me out like I'm a boxer who's been knocked down. It's time. I shut my eyes.

But I know it's a dream. And I want it to end. I hear myself saying 'please wake me when it's all over'.'

I explained to Beardo that I'd heard this track on an album called *Diesel Poems* by Phil Burdett and The New World Troubadours. I felt that it resonated with my own dream world and where its strange stories took me. Beardo felt that the dream represented the deaths and losses that I'd experienced.

Jack also spoke about the night that Dad died. He said that I had told him and Mum that Dad had collapsed in the toilet. He reassured me that I had tried to get their help. So, it wasn't my fault after all.

6

Walking On The Edge

And then I got it. The man in black was Wilko Johnson. He lived down by the tennis courts. He was always dressed in black. Though I love Wilko, he did have a scary stage persona. Doc Beradi thought he represented a symbol of death in my dream.

'Thanks, Doc – I think you may be right. There are some more connections too. I know now that Wilko was that face in the window watching every move I made down on the tennis court. He used to be an English teacher and was a former class-mate of our own English teacher, who me and Wiz called 'the Mentor', at Pouk Hill. The Mentor had brought us this book, 'Coming Up For Air', about a middle-aged man who revisited his old home town where he had a joyous childhood. This was in contrast to the frustrations that he experienced in middle-age. As you know, I was on a mission to try to seek out Wiz on coming back to Binfield, but it hasn't worked out. And in the course of this, I tipped over the edge towards my 'psychic retreat', as you described it. But I've found this whole process of writing a music-related memoir about this mental health 'journey' quite revealing, and I've derived great joy from tapping into the music that goes with the narrative.

This one is a version of a song that Wilko originally recorded with his band, Dr. Feelgood. However, I've already got a Feelgoods track in there already, so I'm playing this later recording instead, here performed with Wilko's next band, The Solid Senders. It was released in 1978, the year I saw him play with the Senders at the Knebworth Festival. It was a great day out. I went there with Wiz. It was probably one of our most enjoyable times together. I wish I could revisit that scene too. I feel that part of me belongs there in that field at Knebworth. And I think that Wiz still belongs there too.'

5

Yesterday Has Gone

Doc Beradi adopted a directive approach when I reflected on my unfulfilled plan to see Wiz again. He felt that I should give up on this. It was a dark November afternoon in his office when he gave me his verdict.

'Lugwin, I understand why you came back to your home town. However, I'd like to counsel that the act of coming back in itself does not guarantee that you will resolve all the upsets that led you back there. And you cannot expect others to co-operate with your ideals. In fact, there is only so much rectifying of the past that you can ever hope to achieve. I'd suggest that the point is simply to understand it. You cannot hope to change it too. It's a waste of your energies and it will probably only lead to you becoming dispirited once again. I would suggest that, for your own good, you need to relinquish this goal. For whatever reasons, Wiz has decided not to respond to your entreaties for your renewed contact. I know that it is a great shame for you but there are some things and people that we have to let go. This may seem a bit brutal but I think that you need to protect yourself from any misplaced hopes here.'

'I've been thinking about what you said last week, Doc. It made me think of this one by Marc Almond and P.J. Proby, released in '96. It's a tough statement to accept. But I get what you were telling me. You have to watch out for hope. And not allow it to lead you into any misguided activity. Thank you.

You've generally let me figure it out for myself with a few cues and clues along the way. This time you probably needed to pull me up on this particular cause though. There really is no point harking back to a friendship that died all that time ago. I know that I've felt guilty about what happened even though things weren't as he probably thought. But I can't do anything about how he feels about it. Though I can derive some comfort from knowing that I tried.

This time spent here at Speedwell, this evaluation with you of what has happened… well, maybe, I can think of it as a watershed now. It's time to think of the future. I guess the demons of the past always stay with us to some extent but the trick is to keep them in their place and not let them inhibit us from getting on with life in the here and now. Anyway, as I used to say in my DJ role, it's time for less talk and more music…'

4

Debris

I've been sending Ray a few cassette broadcasts since he brought up a whole box of my tapes from Harbour Head. It's something that I can do in the quiet of my room here. Apart from a few interruptions, like when one of the nurses comes in and checks on how I am, I can assemble them without distraction. It's been good for me. Along with the tracks that I identify for the sessions with Doc Beradi, this recording process helps me to connect with how I'm feeling. I like to keep a copy too before I send the original off as a way of keeping track of developments. It's like a musical diary.

'Hey Ray, I don't know if I ever told you about this one. It's a B-side, probably the best B-side ever recorded. It's the flip of the Faces' 'Stay With Me', released in late '71, and it was a hit in early '72. I love it. It's probably my favourite record. It's a Ronnie Lane song and he's on lead vocals, with Rod Stewart backing. I find it really evocative and it reminds me of you these days. How you're a hero to me and also my good friend.

Thanks so much for looking after my Oscar and for all you've done this last year. I really don't think I'd have managed without your support. Life's okay here. I've been busy doing a few recordings as part of my therapy. The Doc likes me to bring in a song each week for my counselling session. I might even use this one next week. I hope you're okay too and all the guys doing the shows. Anyway, feel free to crank it up and I'll be in touch on this frequency again soon.'

3

Thinking Of You

Donna sent me a card. It said *Thinking of You* on the cover as though it was an 'in deepest sympathy' card. She wrote that Ray had given her my 'care of' address here on Plashet ward when she'd seen him in Harbour Head shortly after she'd got back from the hospital. Her baby boy George weighed in at just over seven pounds, two ounces. It was nice of her to send me a picture. George looked a bonny boy. His eyes were shut but he seemed to be smiling.

I was genuinely pleased for her. I realised that I wasn't thinking about what might have been anymore. I wasn't even bemused that she'd written '*Ben sends his regards.*'

'*I quite like the insouciant feel of this one, Doc. It's by a group called The Colour Field and it came out in '85. It came to mind as a result of a card I received at the week-end. You remember my ex, Donna? Well, she's had some good news...*'

2

End Of A Century

I've not really enjoyed that arrival of the new year pressure for several years now. This year, it's been magnified even more because of the new millennium. It's been quite a relief being away from the madness outside, in here at Speedwell. It's been quiet with a lot of the gang being able to go home for Christmas. I won't be seeing Doc Beradi 'til the new year as he's on holiday but I thought that I'd select this one for his return.

'Don't read anything into the lyrics of this, Doc. It's the title and the fact that we're here, or I am whilst recording this, right at the end of 1999. This band Blur had their moments and though I didn't particularly care for their music, I thought that this track had a certain charm, though I can't define what it is exactly that I like about it.

I just wanted to say thanks for all your help whilst I've been here. Also, I'm sorry that I didn't take my meds after you sent me on my way from the North City Hospital back when I first met you. Maybe we could have avoided all this if I'd done so. I just got caught up with getting out and about in Binfield that day and I regret it now. But I'm not going to dwell on it.

What's happened has happened and there's no point worrying about it.

I'm not one for making new year's resolutions generally but this year feels different. I'm putting an end to all this ruminating on the past. It's time to think of what the future holds instead.'

1

Do You Remember Rock 'n' Roll Radio?

B eardo liked my resolution. He acknowledged that the past is always with us too. And that there will always be reminders of what has gone before. But that doesn't need to shape everything that comes next. I told him that there were aspects of my more immediate past that I'd like to carry with me into the next century, whilst I was still around to enjoy it.

'The way I see it, Doc, is that my very being has been shaped by this love of music. And I know that my DJ persona can take over at times, but there was something special about being 'The Emperor' that gave me a purpose in life. Particularly with that joy of creating your own radio show and your favourite music blaring out over the airwaves. I want that back in my life again.

The thing is, I'm not ready to go back to Harbour Head and maybe run into Donna, her baby and Ben. I don't want to be reminded of those particular disappointments just yet. And I know you see 'The Emperor' as a manifestation of my mental illness but I think of him as being essential to my being. I feel less of the person that I want to be without him being on my wavelength. And I'd just like to play you this one to try to convey some of the joy that I feel doing this radio thing...'

Beardo listened intently when I played him this track from the Ramones' album, *End Of The Century*. He sat up taller as it finished and he smiled at me before delivering his judgement.

'Thank you, Lugwin. I enjoyed that and I think that I get it. I can see that you wish to be 'The Emperor' in order to most enjoy your preferred mode of communication with people. Perhaps living out this Emperor DJ persona gives you a confidence that you may not otherwise possess if you thought of yourself singularly as Lugwin Loggins. And I do agree most definitely that this can appear like a manifestation of your mental illness, yes. I also agree that you need to be careful that this alter ego does not take control of you and you also have to ensure that you can keep your Emperor persona in check. There's enough madness out there without you adding to it.

I'm sure that the olanzapine is helping you to manage this fine balance. And, if you can keep taking the medication when you leave the hospital, I think that this will definitely help you to straddle the delicate dividing line that sometimes exists between insanity and genius.

We have to finish now but I look forward to seeing you next week when we can start to make plans for your future away from here. And I think that you're right. It's probably just as well that you don't return to Harbour Head just now given the circumstances that you described. Maybe your 'After Care' on leaving here can take place around these parts. It will probably be for the best if you can be

266

close to this service and especially to my team. I am fairly sure that this will help to prevent another relapse. Anyway, let's both give it some more thought ahead of next week.'

I felt validated. I also felt like hugging Beardo when I got up to leave but I knew that kind of thing wasn't done in Speedwell. I also knew that I was on the fast track to a different kind of freedom, so long as I accepted the mental health safeguards that Doc Beradi had suggested. I thought once more of Nico's advice about how to survive in psychiatric hospitals from all those years ago. I've just got to remember to keep my head down, shut my mouth and box clever. And I certainly shouldn't think of rocking any boats, not unless they're music ones, until I get out of here.

You can find the sequel to this story in
FM247: Radios In Motion

ACKNOWLEDGEMENTS

With huge thanks to my great friend Andrew Worsdale, the co-author of *FM247: This Is Radio Binfield!*, for his permission to revise our joint work. I'd also like to note that I've adapted Andrew's original work in the chapters of 'Tiny Children', 'Everyone's Gone To The Moon', 'Solitaire' and in the last paragraph of 'Louise', in the completion of this novella. To paraphrase Alice Cooper's reference to Arthur Brown: no Andrew Worsdale, no Lugwin Loggins.

With great thanks to James Essinger, founder and managing director of The Conrad Press Ltd, for his faith in this effort and his helpful advice towards the completion of the final version of this novella.

With joyous gratitude to Alan Furneaux for the use of his painting 'Moonlight over Porthleven' for the front cover of this book.

Many thanks to Zoe Verner of The Conrad Press Ltd for guiding me through the formatting and proof-reading process ahead of publication.

Big thanks to Rachael and Nat Ravenlock of The Book Typesetters for their work on the book's cover design and the presentation of this work.

Special thanks to the DJs of my younger days, particularly Tony Blackburn, Simon Bates, Johnnie Walker, Steve Wright and the late, great John Peel as well as the hundred musicians/songwriters cited in this book.

With much love and ongoing appreciation of Lisa Spooner for her encouragement and forbearance.

And, of course, many thanks to you for giving this book your time and consideration. I hope that you enjoy it.

Rob Spooner
May, 2022